THE R
S
FLIGHT
MY LIFE BEHIND THE MQ-9 REAPER
John 'Hawkeye' Mitchell

The Reaper's Flight: My Life Behind The MQ-9 Reaper

John 'Hawkeye' Mitchell

Published by Fortis Novum Mundum, 2023.

This is a work of fiction. Similarities to real people, places, or events are entirely coincidental.

THE REAPER'S FLIGHT: MY LIFE BEHIND THE MQ-9 REAPER

First edition. September 11, 2023.

ISBN: 979-8223702559

Written by John 'Hawkeye' Mitchell.

The Reaper's Flight: My Life Behind The MQ-9 Reaper

By

Lt. Col. John 'Hawkeye' Mitchell

Table of Contents

Description

Diving deep into the intricate world of Remotely Piloted Aircrafts (RPAs), Commander John "Hawkeye" Mitchell paints a vivid canvas of aerial warfare in the 21st century in "The Reaper's Flight". Tracing the legacy of aviation—from the first unmanned crafts to the technologically superior drones of today—Mitchell's detailed expositions shed light on the myriad developments and strategic shifts.

Amidst the backdrop of an evolving military landscape, Mitchell's narrative is punctuated with personal anecdotes from his illustrious career, spanning covert operations in the Middle East to high-stake surveillance missions in Asia. But, much like the analytical dissections of grand empires of yesteryears, Mitchell delves deeper, probing the ethics of remote warfare. He questions, with a critical lens, the paradoxical relationship between man and machine, and the emotional cost of waging war from a distance.

Drawing from a reservoir of classified missions, operational details, and personal experiences, Mitchell's voice emerges as one deeply informed yet continually inquisitive. He navigates the reader through the labyrinth of global geopolitics, highlighting the nuanced challenges faced by RPAs, their transformative impact on modern warfare, and the potential trajectory of their evolution.

"The Reaper's Flight" isn't just an account—it's an exploration. One that not only chronicles the changing face of warfare but also underscores the lessons, pitfalls, and the uncharted potential of what lies ahead in the domain of remote aviation. Through Mitchell's eyes, we are offered a unique vantage point—a glimpse into the past, a reflection on the present, and a vision for the future of warfare.

The key principles of the laws of war are necessity, distinction, and proportionality in the use of force. Drone attacks and targeted killings serve these principles better than any use of force that can be imagined.

—Richard Pildes

Foreword

In a rapidly evolving era of warfare, where the lines between man and machine often blur, it becomes pivotal for us to understand the intricate nexus of technology, ethics, strategy, and human spirit. This nexus has been brilliantly decoded by none other than Lt. Col. John 'Hawkeye' Mitchell in "The Reaper's Flight". As the founder and CEO of Greyhat Intelligence & Investigative Solutions and having authored several titles on the subject, I've traversed the vast landscapes of modern warfare both in the ink of my pen and the core of my operations. Yet, it's rare to come across a narrative that offers such a profoundly personal yet panoramic view of the world of Remotely Piloted Aircrafts (RPAs) as this one.

Having penned works such as 'Eyes in the Sky', which focused on the global significance of UAVs, and 'Algorithmic Warfare', which delved into the intriguing realm of autonomous weapons, I can assertively claim that the uniqueness of "The Reaper's Flight" lies in its genuine firsthand accounts. Mitchell doesn't just provide insights—he has lived through them. Each chapter, each anecdote, and each analysis carries the weight of experiences that only someone of his stature could elucidate.

Lt. Col. John 'Hawkeye' Mitchell is not just an author. He's an American hero. His commitment to his country, to the ethos of his duty, and to the evolving paradigm of modern warfare has made him a beacon of inspiration for countless individuals. He stands tall as an embodiment of American exceptionalism—a figure who has faced the challenges of modern warfare head-on, adapted, and emerged with both lessons and laurels.

In this era, where warfare is not just about soldiers on the ground but also codes on a computer, drones in the sky, and decisions taken from thousands of miles away, it is crucial to have voices like Mitchell's. Voices that resonate with integrity, insight, and indomitable spirit. "The Reaper's Flight" isn't just a book—it's a testament to the mettle and mindset of one of America's finest.

I commend Lt. Col. Mitchell for bringing to life a narrative that is as compelling as it is informative. It's a privilege to introduce this remarkable tome to readers worldwide. As you delve into these pages, you're not just reading—you're journeying alongside an American legend.

Josh Luberisse,
Founder & CEO,
Greyhat Intelligence
& Investigative Solutions

Introduction

In the vast expanse of the blue sky, a faint hum emerges, often too distant to be seen by the naked eye, but its presence is undeniable. From the dense forests of Asia to the arid deserts of the Middle East and the urban landscapes of the West, Remotely Piloted Aircrafts (RPAs), commonly referred to as drones, have reshaped the very fabric of modern warfare, surveillance, and aerial reconnaissance.

The dawn of the 21st century was marked by a surge in technological advancements, with digital revolutions affecting nearly every facet of our lives. Among the most groundbreaking of these developments is the evolution and deployment of RPAs. What began as rudimentary devices with limited capabilities, primarily used for basic reconnaissance, have now transformed into sophisticated machines capable of intricate maneuvers, long-endurance flights, and precision strikes.

Yet, as with every leap in technology, the journey of RPAs is more than just circuits, wings, and rotors. It's a tale of human ingenuity, ethical dilemmas, geopolitical repercussions, and a glimpse into the future of conflict, surveillance, and peacekeeping. In "The Reaper's Flight: A Pilot's Journey in Remotely Piloted Aircrafts," we aim to delve deep into this dynamic world, dissecting both its marvels and its controversies.

This book is not merely a chronicle of the development and deployment of RPAs but a journey into the cockpit alongside the pilots who operate them. We'll be exploring the mindscape of those who sit miles away, yet have the power to make split-second decisions that can alter the course of conflicts, impact global geopolitics, and, at times, decide between life and death.

Drawing inspiration from prominent thinkers, military strategists, and RPA pilots, our journey will traverse the grey areas of ethics, the challenges posed to international law, and the endless debates on the implications of 'push-button' warfare. We will look into the eyes of soldiers on the ground, whose lives are intertwined with the silent guardians above, and listen to the voices of innocent civilians, whose lives have been irrevocably changed by the drone era.

The RPAs' narrative is also one of constant innovation. As we progress, we will witness the remarkable technological advancements that have expanded the RPAs' scope far beyond military applications. From agriculture and disaster management to urban planning and environmental conservation, drones are gradually becoming omnipresent, affecting our daily lives in ways we might not even be aware of.

However, it's essential to understand that while the RPA evolution is undeniably exciting and transformative, it's not without its shadows.

The ease and detachment with which conflicts can now be approached, thanks to drones, brings forth a plethora of moral, ethical, and legal questions. These are issues that societies and nations grapple with, even as RPAs continue to evolve at breakneck speeds.

As we embark on this enlightening voyage through the skies and corridors of power, our objective is clear: to offer a comprehensive, unbiased, and deeply insightful exploration of the world of RPAs. From the highs of technological marvels to the lows of human tragedies, from the thrill of innovation to the weight of responsibility, "The Reaper's Flight" is set to take you on a roller-coaster of emotions, knowledge, and introspection.

So, fasten your seatbelts, as we take off into the vast, intricate, and endlessly fascinating universe of Remotely Piloted Aircrafts. Welcome aboard.

My Introduction to Remotely Piloted Aircrafts (RPAs)

In the vast realm of aviation, few developments have captured the collective imagination and elicited such a range of emotions as the ascent of Remotely Piloted Aircrafts, often referred to as drones. These mechanical birds, soaring silently in the skies, heralded not just a technological advancement but a paradigm shift in the very essence of how we perceive aerial warfare and surveillance. My personal foray into the world of RPAs was not just a mere introduction to a piece of machinery, but rather, an immersion into a fascinating era of aviation history that was rapidly unfurling before our eyes.

During the early days of my career, the skies were predominantly commanded by traditional manned aircraft. As a young aviator, my dreams were filled with the roar of jet engines, the tactile feedback of a control stick, and the exhilarating sensation of breaking through clouds, feeling the sun warm my face. The world of aviation was as much about touch and feel as it was about skill and precision. However, as the years progressed, there were murmurs of something new on the horizon, something that threatened to revolutionize the very core of aerial operations. The Remotely Piloted Aircraft was that revolution, an innovation that was about to challenge the status quo and redefine the boundaries of what was considered possible in the sky.

It was during a routine training seminar that I first encountered an RPA. At first glance, it seemed like a modestly sized, strangely designed aircraft. Without the usual cockpit and absent the quintessential features that typified a conventional plane, it appeared almost otherworldly. But beneath this unassuming exterior lay an intricate tapestry of technological marvels. The drone was a fusion of advanced aerodynamics, cutting-edge electronics, and sophisticated software algorithms, all working in tandem to achieve feats previously deemed unimaginable.

As I delved deeper into the world of RPAs, I quickly realized that these were not just automated machines but intricately designed systems that required a new kind of pilot. A pilot who, rather than being physically present inside the aircraft, was firmly grounded, operating the machine from miles away. The experience was both alien and familiar. On one hand, I missed the tactile sensations, the G-forces, and the immediate feedback that a traditional cockpit provided. On the other hand, the RPA offered a panoramic view, a detachment that allowed for more calculated decisions, and the undeniable advantage of not placing a human life directly in harm's way during combat or reconnaissance missions.

Navigating the digital interface of an RPA was akin to playing a highly sophisticated video game, yet with real-world implications. The joystick and multiple screens replaced the yoke and physical instruments. The initial skepticism I felt began to ebb as I underwent rigorous training sessions. These sessions were meticulously designed to ensure that pilots could seamlessly transition from the physical cockpit to the digital interface of the drone. Every simulated mission, every drill, was an exercise in recalibrating my instincts, learning to trust the screens before me, and understanding the nuanced dynamics of remotely piloted flight.

But beyond the technicalities, my introduction to RPAs was also a profound journey of introspection. The very essence of what it meant to be a pilot was undergoing a transformation. The skies, once a realm of tactile exploration, were now being charted digitally. The drone, with its myriad sensors and cameras, could perceive the environment in ways the human eye could not. Infrared imaging, night vision, and high-resolution cameras provided a vantage point that was unparalleled. The horizon of possibilities was expanding, and I was at the very epicenter of this evolution.

As the months turned into years, my proficiency with RPAs grew. The initial apprehension gave way to a deep-seated appreciation for these machines. They were not just tools; they were the future. A future where reconnaissance missions could be conducted without the risk of human casualty, where intricate operations could be executed with surgical precision, and where the very definition of air superiority was being rewritten.

My introduction to Remotely Piloted Aircrafts was not merely an adaptation to a new technological tool; it was a transformative experience. It reshaped my understanding of aviation, challenged my preconceived notions, and ultimately, enriched my journey as a pilot. As I look back, I am filled with a sense of gratitude for having been a part of this monumental shift in aviation history, a chapter that will undoubtedly be etched in the annals of time as a turning point, a moment when we transcended conventional boundaries and soared into a new era.

Chapter 1: The Dawn of RPAs

A Brief History of Drones and RPAs

The tapestry of human history is replete with our ceaseless endeavors to conquer the skies. From the mythical wax wings of Icarus to the tangible genius of the Wright brothers, mankind's obsession with flight has been an indelible part of our collective journey. As with most technological evolutions, aviation, too, witnessed its moments of profound transformation. Among these milestones, the birth and evolution of Remotely Piloted Aircrafts (RPAs) and drones command a special significance, marking a paradigm shift in how we interact with the very fabric of the skies.

While today's sophisticated drones, with their advanced sensors and superior maneuverability, seem like futuristic marvels, the origins of unmanned flight can be traced back to much humbler beginnings. It was during the throes of World War I that the seeds of the idea were first sown. The exigencies of warfare, with its insatiable demand for innovation, birthed the earliest incarnations of drones. These rudimentary contraptions, more mechanical than electronic, were designed as aerial targets for training anti-aircraft gunners. Their inception was less about sophisticated warfare and more about meeting an immediate tactical need. Nevertheless, the foundation had been laid.

The interwar years saw sporadic advancements in drone technology. However, it was World War II that accelerated the growth of RPAs, when the exigencies of combat necessitated enhanced reconnaissance capabilities. The United States, understanding the potential of such machines, embarked on a series of projects. One such endeavor yielded the "Radioplane," an early drone used for training anti-aircraft gunners. These devices were not just mere static targets; they were remotely controlled, marking an early foray into the realm of RPAs.

As the world emerged from the shadows of the Second World War and entered the cold, strategic standoff of the Cold War, the imperatives changed. Espionage and intelligence-gathering became paramount. The high-stakes environment of this era, where information was as potent a weapon as any missile, catalyzed the evolution of drones from mere training tools to sophisticated reconnaissance machines. Their ability to venture into hostile territories without risking human lives made them invaluable assets in the intricate chess game of global politics.

It was during this period that the term 'drone' started becoming synonymous with reconnaissance. These RPAs, equipped with cameras and communication devices, would undertake clandestine missions, gathering vital intelligence and relaying it back. Their silent presence in the skies above hostile territories represented a new kind of warfare—one that was less about direct confrontation and more about gathering information, anticipating moves, and countering them.

Yet, as is the nature of technological advancement, the landscape of drone technology was soon to witness another transformation. The dawn of the 21st century heralded the age of armed drones. No longer were these machines just the silent observers; they had evolved into formidable tools of precision strikes. The transition of drones from mere surveillance tools to armed combatants was both a technological marvel and a subject of intense debate. Ethical, political, and strategic dimensions intertwined as drones began to play a pivotal role in conflict zones, especially in the Middle East.

The very fabric of warfare was altered. Remote strikes became feasible, and suddenly, the decision to deploy force could be made without the immediate risk of human casualty, at least on one side. This dynamic changed not only military strategies but also the politics of warfare. Leaders, now equipped with a means to strike without deploying troops, found themselves grappling with the moral implications of such power.

From their rudimentary beginnings in the early 20th century to their sophisticated present, RPAs have traversed an extraordinary journey. This evolution was not just about the machines themselves but also about the changing ethos of global conflicts and the ever-shifting paradigms of technological advancements.

In retrospect, the history of drones and RPAs is a testament to human ingenuity. It speaks of our relentless quest to push boundaries, to innovate, and to redefine the realms of possibility. As these machines soared in the skies, they not only charted new territories but also mirrored our own aspirations, fears, dilemmas, and ambitions. They became, in many ways, a reflection of the epoch, capturing the zeitgeist of an era that was rapidly hurtling towards a future where technology and humanity would become increasingly intertwined.

The story of drones and RPAs is not just a chronicle of machines; it is, in essence, a narrative of human progress, of our ceaseless endeavor to ascend, to explore, and to conquer. It is a tale that underscores the intertwined destinies of man and machine, a relationship that promises to shape the contours of the future in ways we are only beginning to fathom.

The latter half of the 20th century witnessed a world in flux, with geopolitical landscapes shifting and new technologies emerging at breakneck speeds. In this whirlwind of change, drones and RPAs found themselves at the intersection of innovation and necessity. As nations grappled with the new realities of a post-war world, these unmanned aerial vehicles (UAVs) provided solutions to some of the most pressing challenges of the age.

As Cold War tensions simmered, so too did the race for technological supremacy between the superpowers. Drones, with their innate ability to operate without a human on board, became emblematic of this drive for superiority. They epitomized the very essence of remote warfare—a tool that could penetrate enemy lines, gather intelligence, and even launch strikes, all without risking the lives of pilots.

The Vietnam War further underscored the value of RPAs. The thick jungles and guerilla tactics employed by the Viet Cong made traditional reconnaissance challenging. Drones emerged as a solution, silently hovering above the dense canopy, capturing images, and providing commanders with crucial information about enemy positions and movements. Their success in this theater underscored their potential, laying the groundwork for their expanded role in future conflicts.

As the decades rolled on and the 20th century gave way to the 21st, drones underwent a metamorphosis. Technological advancements in miniaturization, artificial intelligence, and communications enabled these machines to become smarter, more autonomous, and increasingly versatile. They were no longer confined to military applications. RPAs started making their presence felt in civilian sectors, from agriculture and environmental monitoring to disaster relief and entertainment.

But it was the Global War on Terror, sparked by the tragic events of September 11, 2001, that truly underscored the strategic significance of armed drones. In the rugged terrains of Afghanistan and the volatile regions of Pakistan's border areas, drones like the MQ-1 Predator and the MQ-9 Reaper became household names. They offered the ability to track, monitor, and neutralize threats with unprecedented precision, changing the calculus of counterterrorism operations. These missions, often carried out in regions where it was perilous to deploy ground troops or manned aircraft, exemplified the utility of RPAs in asymmetrical warfare.

MQ-1 Predator, armed with AGM-114 Hellfire Missiles

MQ-9 Reaper

Yet, with this newfound power came newfound dilemmas. The very advantages that made drones so compelling—precision, reduced risk to human operators, and the ability to loiter over areas for extended periods—also raised profound ethical and moral questions. The nature of remote warfare meant that the immediacy and visceral realities of combat were somewhat abstracted. Decisions to launch strikes from thousands of miles away in the comfort of a control room brought about debates on the very nature of warfare, accountability, and the value of human life.

This introspection, coupled with the rapid advancements in drone technology, marked the beginning of a new chapter in the history of RPAs. As the technology became more accessible, nations around the world began to recognize the strategic value of drones. From surveillance missions in the disputed South China Sea territories to anti-piracy operations off the Horn of Africa, RPAs became ubiquitous. Their global proliferation underscored their significance in the tapestry of modern warfare and diplomacy.

In tracing this rich tapestry, from the rudimentary radio-controlled targets of the World Wars to the sophisticated, multi-role drones of today, one witnesses not just the evolution of a technology but the transformation of global conflict paradigms. The emergence and ascent of drones and RPAs offer a lens into the broader shifts in geopolitics, strategy, and the eternal human quest for dominance and security.

The tale of drones, much like the broader human endeavor, is one of progress and reflection, of ambition and introspection. As we stand on the cusp of an era where autonomous machines and artificial intelligence promise to redefine the boundaries of the possible, the journey of drones and RPAs serves as a poignant reminder of our own journey—a journey marked by brilliance, innovation, dilemmas, and the undying human spirit to soar ever higher.

Chapter 2: First Encounter with the Reaper

My Initial Perceptions

In the vast, intricate tapestry of my life, colored by myriad experiences and encounters, there stands out one thread, vibrant and unyielding, that of my first rendezvous with the Reaper. This encounter was no poetic tryst with a hooded figure wielding a scythe but rather with a beast of metal and might—the MQ-9 Reaper, a remotely piloted aircraft (RPA) known for its unparalleled prowess in the skies. That initial encounter, embedded deeply in the annals of my memory, resonates with a melange of wonder, trepidation, and the profound realization of the changing paradigms of warfare.

U.S. Air Force MQ-9A Reaper Drone

It was a crisp morning, with the first light of dawn splintering the horizon, when I found myself standing at the threshold of a new era, both for me personally and for aerial combat as we knew it. As I approached the tarmac, the sight before me was one of sheer magnitude—a sleek, predator-esque silhouette against the vast expanse of the runway. The Reaper, with its elongated wings, its sensors that seemed to gaze into the soul, and its payload that spoke of deadly precision, stood there, not just as a marvel of engineering but as a testament to human ingenuity and, some might say, our penchant for darker pursuits.

Having cut my teeth on traditional aircraft, those that demanded the physical presence of a pilot, this machine before me was an enigma. It had the capability to mete out death from above, all while its operator sat thousands of miles away, nestled safely in a command center. The idea was both awe-inspiring and, to be perfectly honest, a tad unnerving. I quipped to a colleague, "It's like playing a video game, just with higher stakes and no extra lives." We shared a knowing chuckle, but beneath that veneer of dark humor lay an acknowledgment of the gravity of the Reaper's capabilities.

The jargon that echoed around me—terms like "GCS" (Ground Control Station), "sensor ball," and "fire-and-forget Hellfire missiles"—all painted a picture of an intricate ballet of technology, strategy, and raw power. As a newcomer to the realm of RPAs, every tidbit of information, every acronym, was a dive into the depths of a brave new world. The learning curve was steep, and every briefing felt like drinking from a firehose. But amidst the deluge of data, my military training held me in good stead, acting as an anchor, grounding me to the ethos and principles that are the bedrock of any form of combat, manned or unmanned.

But perhaps the most intriguing, and somewhat paradoxical, aspect of the Reaper was the dichotomy it presented. Here was a machine that could surveil an area for hours on end, gather intelligence, and then, with the same dispassionate precision, deliver destruction. And yet, its very name—Reaper—brought with it connotations of finality, of the grim harvest of souls. It's quite the branding strategy, I mused, naming an RPA after the very embodiment of death. But then again, in the world of military branding, subtlety was rarely the order of the day.

As the day wore on and I delved deeper into the operational nuances of the Reaper, I couldn't help but reflect on the broader implications of such a tool in our arsenal. The MQ-9 was not just an aircraft; it was a symbol. A symbol of a world where technology had blurred the lines between the combatant and the console, between the frontline and the command center. In this brave new world, the age-old dictums of warfare were being rewritten, and as I stood there, at the vanguard of this transformation, the weight of responsibility was palpable.

Yet, as the sun dipped below the horizon and the Reaper's silhouette merged with the gathering darkness, a wry thought crossed my mind. If this was the future of warfare, with machines, algorithms, and remote operations, then perhaps the old adage needed a slight revision. It was no longer just about having "eyes in the sky." Now, it was about having "reapers in the sky"—and as I'd soon learn, these reapers played for keeps.

Training for a New Kind of Flight

One might imagine that having an extensive background in piloting traditional aircraft would pave the golden pathway to mastering the intricacies of operating an RPA. But I quickly realized, as I embarked on the labyrinthine journey of training for the MQ-9 Reaper, that this was an entirely different beast, presenting challenges that were both novel and nuanced. The arena had shifted from the palpable confines of a cockpit to the virtual dimensions of screens and joysticks. Instead of soaring through the skies, I was now poised to traverse them from a stationary, grounded vantage point.

It began, as most military endeavors do, with the onslaught of paperwork and pre-training briefings. One might jest that the military has an acronym for everything, and the world of RPAs was no exception. ISR (Intelligence, Surveillance, and Reconnaissance), Loitering Munition, and the ever-present PID (Positive Identification) became not just jargon, but the vernacular of this new realm. As I delved into the literature, manuals, and thick binders that seemed to have been created to induce a certain level of dread, a fellow trainee mused, "You'd think they were prepping us for a PhD in Drone-ology!" A moment of levity in an otherwise intense initiation.

The actual training sessions, however, were a stark departure from the dreary drone of paperwork. The simulator—a cutting-edge contraption that mimicked the MQ-9's operations—was the proverbial playground. Here, amidst a myriad of screens, dials, and buttons, I was to hone my skills, transitioning from pilot to operator. As I settled into the ergonomically designed chair, joystick in hand, I couldn't help but draw parallels to an arcade game, albeit one with far graver implications. "It's like Pac-Man," quipped an instructor, "just that our ghosts are very real, and they don't want to play."

Yet, as the training progressed, it became evident that the Reaper was not merely a sophisticated toy. Its multifaceted capabilities demanded a depth of understanding and a finesse that was at once intricate and intuitive. The dance between navigating, targeting, and monitoring required a delicate balance—a symphony of man and machine.

While the actual maneuvering of the Reaper had its complexities, the true challenge lay in decision-making. The detachment, brought on by the remote nature of RPA operations, brought forth ethical quandaries. In a traditional aircraft, the immediacy of conflict, the palpable danger, often streamlined decisions. But in the sanitized environment of the Ground Control Station, every move, every missile release, became a pondered decision. The vast distance between the operator and the operational field somehow magnified the weight of responsibility.

There were moments of levity, of course. During a particularly challenging simulated mission, where multiple 'enemy combatants' seemed to spring from every virtual nook and cranny, a colleague humorously remarked, "Feels like we're in a twisted game of Whack-A-Mole, doesn't it?" And indeed, there were elements of the surreal, the uncanny, as we maneuvered our virtual craft, striking at pixelated targets, all the while aware of the stark real-world implications of our actions.

The weeks of training melded into a blur of rigorous sessions, debriefings, and the ever-present camaraderie that forms amongst those who tread the same challenging path. Shared frustrations over mismanaged simulations, collective triumphs over successful 'missions', and the gallows humor that emerged from the juxtaposition of the gravity of our task and the video game-like milieu of our training, all wove the fabric of our shared experience.

By the culmination of our training, as I looked back, the journey from novice to adept seemed both arduous and enlightening. The MQ-9 Reaper, once a daunting behemoth, had become an extension of our strategic intent. We had been molded, not just to operate a machine, but to navigate the intricate interplay of ethics, strategy, and technology.

As I emerged from the training center, badge of qualification in hand, the enormity of the task ahead weighed heavily. Yet, intertwined with that weight was a sense of purpose, a conviction that, equipped with our newfound skills and the Reaper at our command, we were poised to redefine the contours of modern warfare. And while the road ahead promised challenges aplenty, there was solace in the knowledge that we were pioneers, charting a course through uncharted skies.

Training for the MQ-9 Reaper was akin to drinking from a firehose—overwhelming, intense, but essential. Yet, for all the simulated flights and controlled scenarios, the real education came from the unexpected moments, the situations that weren't in the manuals, the split-second decisions that didn't allow the luxury of contemplation.

As days turned to nights and back to days again, the Ground Control Station (GCS) became both our prison and our sanctuary. The relentless hum of machinery, the glow of multiple screens, and the hushed conversations peppered with military slang formed the backdrop to our nascent experiences as RPA pilots. "Remember," an experienced operator once remarked with a mischievous glint in his eye, "this isn't Top Gun. Our need for speed is more about bandwidth than breaking sound barriers."

While the technology was cutting edge, the ambiance inside the GCS had its own archaic charm. Amidst the whir of technology, old school pilot traditions found their way in. Squadron patches, unit mottos, and the occasional prank served as reminders of the storied legacy we were a part of. One particular instance comes to mind: a fellow trainee, after a flawless simulated sortie, found his chair replaced with an ejection seat mockup, complete with a sign saying, "In case of another perfect mission, pull the lever." Dark humor, as it turned out, was a coping mechanism, an essential balm to the constant gravity of our training and subsequent missions.

The complexity of the MQ-9 Reaper's systems required not only an intimate knowledge of its technological facets but also an intrinsic understanding of its tactical applications. We learned to discern, for instance, between a gathering of villagers and a congregation of enemy combatants from thousands of feet above, using minute cues and subtle differences. The Reaper's cameras, with their uncanny ability to zoom into the most minute details, turned us into airborne detectives, always searching for that one clue, that telltale sign that separated an ordinary scenario from a potential threat.

But it wasn't all grim determination and steely focus. The rapport between operators, sensor operators, and the intelligence teams added a human touch to this world of machines. Debates over the best techniques to employ, disagreements over interpretations of a situation, and the shared elation or disappointment over a mission's outcome—all these interactions wove a tapestry of relationships. These bonds, often forged in the crucible of high-stakes situations, became our anchor, our touchstone in the often-disorienting world of remote warfare.

One could argue that our training was as much psychological as it was technical. Engaging an enemy from a cockpit, with the immediacy of conflict and the adrenaline of a dogfight, is a vastly different experience from doing so via a joystick and screen, thousands of miles away from the theater of operations. This detachment, while offering safety, also posed unique challenges. The dissonance between conducting lethal operations during one's shift and then heading home to the mundanities of everyday life required a mental fortitude that was constantly emphasized throughout our training.

As weeks melded into months, our proficiency grew, but so did our respect for the responsibility that came with it. With every simulated strike, every surveillance mission, we were constantly reminded of the real-world implications of our actions. Each decision, each movement of the joystick, bore consequences that reverberated far beyond our GCS.

By the end of our training journey, we had transformed. No longer mere pilots, we had become operators, custodians of a technology that was reshaping the future of warfare. The journey had been arduous, fraught with challenges both anticipated and unforeseen. Yet, with the

Reaper as our steed, and armed with the knowledge and experiences of our training, we stood ready. Ready to navigate the vast, uncharted expanse of the modern battlespace, bearing the weight of our newfound responsibilities with pride and determination.

Chapter 3: The Flight Deck Behind Closed Doors

The Simulator: Ground Training

Photo: General Atomics Aeronautical Systems' Certifiable Ground Control Station[1]. Credit: GA-ASI

If one were to ask the average individual what they imagined the interior of an RPA training simulator to look like, visions of sci-fi movies or high-end video game setups might immediately come to mind. However, the reality of the Ground Control Station (GCS) simulator, where pilots cut their teeth on the MQ-9 Reaper without ever leaving terra firma, is both more mundane and yet immeasurably more intricate than most cinematic portrayals.

The first encounter with the GCS simulator often left aspiring pilots wide-eyed. It was a room filled with a delicate balance of cutting-edge technology and familiar aviation instruments, creating an ambiance that was part high-tech command center and part traditional

1. https://www.ga-asi.com/ground-control-stations/certifiable-ground-control-station

cockpit. Upon entering, one would be greeted by the gentle hum of computer systems and the soft glow of multiple displays, each one providing a window into a virtual world where pilots could hone their skills without the risk of real-world consequences.

The simulator, affectionately dubbed "The Sandbox" by more seasoned pilots, was a place of both endless possibilities and unyielding exactness. It could replicate almost any scenario, from a calm reconnaissance mission over a quiet village to the high-intensity drama of a hot pursuit in hostile territory. Yet, with each simulation came an unforgiving level of precision, demanding that pilots respond with accuracy, efficiency, and an acute awareness of the consequences of their decisions.

It's important to understand that the role of the simulator was not merely to replicate real-world flight conditions. Its primary purpose was to forge the mental and emotional resilience required of an RPA pilot. The Sandbox was where pilots learned the art of patience, the importance of discernment, and the weight of responsibility. It was a place where mistakes were expected, dissected, and learned from—a safe haven where every failure was an opportunity for growth.

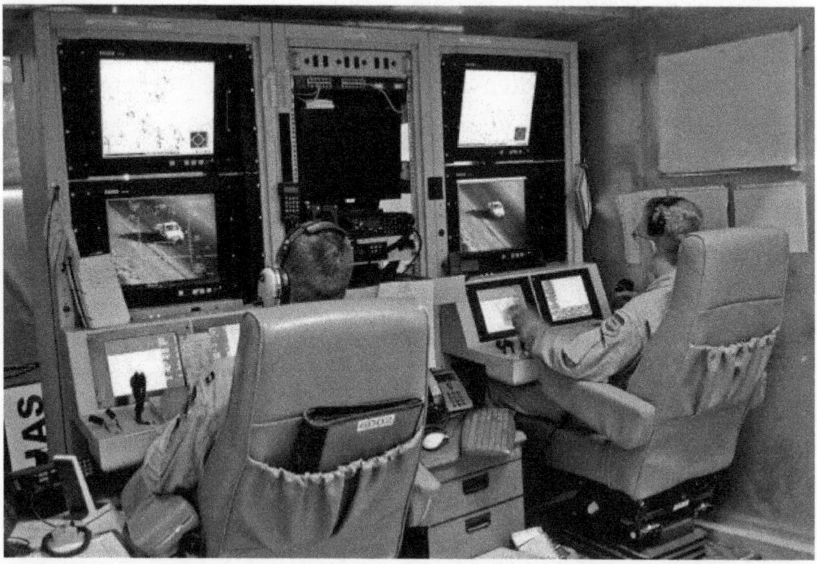

Photo: An Air Force RPA Pilot (left) and sensor operator control GA-ASI's MQ-1 Predator RPA in 2005. Credit: U.S. Air Force[1]

As trainees progressed, the simulator scenarios became more multifaceted, introducing a plethora of variables to contend with. There might be sudden shifts in weather patterns, unexpected equipment malfunctions, or the introduction of hostile entities. Such meticulously designed complexities aimed to push pilots beyond their limits, forcing them to think on their feet and adapt in real-time. Every session was a dance of fingers on controls, eyes scanning screens, and ears tuned to every beep, buzz, or piece of information relayed by the simulator's artificial intelligence.

---

1. https://www.af.mil/News/Photos.aspx?igphoto=2000461305

Between sessions, debriefings often took longer than the simulations themselves. Detailed analyses of each decision, movement, and outcome ensued, often accompanied by heated debates among trainees and instructors. "Why did you choose to engage there?" "What made you divert from the original flight path?" "How did you miss that civilian?" These probing questions weren't intended to berate but to refine, to transform raw talent into precision and instinct into calculated decision-making.

An essential part of this training was also focused on the symbiotic relationship between the pilot and the sensor operator. In the simulated environment, this partnership was nurtured and tested. The two had to operate as a single unit, a cohesive entity where communication was seamless and trust absolute. Often, the success of a mission hinged on this intricate ballet of coordination and mutual reliance.

Over time, a transformation occurred. Trainees entered the simulator as individuals, laden with preconceptions and personal flight habits. Yet, after countless hours in The Sandbox, they emerged as part of a larger entity—a cog in the vast machinery of remote warfare. They had become acutely aware of the broader strategic picture, recognizing their role not just as pilots of a machine but as instruments of policy and strategy.

The GCS simulator was more than a training tool. It was an essential crucible where skills were sharpened, character was forged, and the future guardians of the skies were molded. Here, in this virtual realm, pilots learned not only the mechanics of operating the Reaper but also the profound responsibility that came with wielding such formidable power.

My First Flight: Anxiety and Elation

There exists a curious juxtaposition in the human psyche when one is perched on the precipice of history, both personal and broader. It's a delicate dance between the paralyzing grip of anxiety and the soaring wings of elation. For me, that dance found its stage on the day of my first MQ-9 Reaper flight. It was an experience awash with a myriad of emotions, from the profound respect for the machinery I was to command to the weight of the responsibility that it symbolically bore upon its metallic wings.

To the uninitiated observer, the commencement of an RPA flight might seem underwhelming, devoid of the tangible thrill that accompanies the roar of jet engines or the rush of wind against metal. But the truth is far more nuanced. Within the confines of the Ground Control Station (GCS), there's an unmistakable tension, an electric charge in the air that's palpable. It's an atmosphere thick with anticipation, where every glance exchanged between the pilot and the sensor operator is a silent conversation, each understanding the magnitude of the task ahead.

For me, the experience began much before I stepped into the GCS. The night prior was a restless one, filled with a cascade of dreams, some exhilarating, others foreboding. The knowledge that I would soon be at the helm of a multi-million dollar piece of technology, equipped with the capability to surveil, to gather intelligence, and when needed, to strike, was overwhelming. The Reaper wasn't just a marvel of engineering; it was a potent emblem of the age we lived in—a testament to mankind's quest for mastery over the skies and the paradoxical union of distance and intimacy in modern warfare.

As dawn broke, I found myself walking toward the GCS, my footsteps resonating with a mix of trepidation and excitement. The initial procedures felt almost robotic, a series of well-rehearsed steps that I had executed numerous times in the simulator. But today was different. Today, those virtual pixels would transition into the tangible, the simulated hum of engines would morph into the real-world purr of a powerhouse ready to take to the skies.

The process of initiating the flight was methodical, each step punctuated by checks and confirmations. My fingers danced over the controls with a mix of practiced ease and cautious reverence. With the sensor operator by my side, we ran through the checklist, ensuring that every system was operational, every protocol observed. The crescendo of activity culminated in the moment of takeoff—a moment that, despite its virtual nature, had all the gravitas of a traditional flight.

As the Reaper soared, the world beneath unfolded in a panoramic spectacle. Through the high-definition feed, landscapes morphed from abstract patches of color to discernible features, every nook and cranny laid bare by the unblinking eye of the drone. It was an intoxicating feeling, the sensation of omnipotence combined with the realization of being a tiny speck in the grand tapestry of the universe.

Yet, with that elation came an undercurrent of anxiety. Each decision carried weight. Every maneuver bore implications not just for the mission but for the broader geopolitical landscape. The lines between right and wrong, between friend and foe, were often blurred, and the stakes were incredibly high. The Reaper's capabilities were vast, but they were not infallible. The onus was on us, the human components, to bridge the gap, to ensure that technology served its intended purpose without overstepping its bounds.

The flight's duration was a symphony of highs and lows, moments of sheer awe juxtaposed with periods of intense concentration. There were instances where the beauty of our planet, viewed from high above, took my breath away. But there were also moments of sobering realization, where the gravity of my role, and the power and responsibility vested in the MQ-9 Reaper, became all too real.

As the flight drew to a close and the Reaper made its descent, a wave of emotions washed over me. There was pride in the successful completion of the mission, relief that the myriad potential pitfalls had been navigated without incident, and a profound sense of gratitude for the opportunity to be a part of something so much larger than oneself.

Photo: Ground control stations receive and process data collected by the RPA's sensors and subsystems in real time, allowing military personnel to adjust operations accordingly and make key decisions quickly. Credit: Air Force Technology

In the end, my first flight was more than just a technical exercise. It was a rite of passage, a journey that delved deep into the human spirit's recesses. It was an exploration of the delicate balance between man and machine, between the insatiable quest for progress and the timeless virtues of wisdom and restraint. It was, in every sense, a dance between anxiety and elation.

The immediate aftermath of the flight was a blur. The deafening silence of the GCS post-mission was punctuated only by the low hum of the machinery and the rhythmic tapping of keyboards as logs were meticulously updated. The adrenaline which had surged throughout the mission was now subsiding, replaced by a mental exhaustion that seemed to seep into every pore. Yet, amidst this fatigue, there was an undeniable undercurrent of exhilaration—a sensation that we had, for those few hours, touched the very fringes of the future.

Exiting the GCS, the world outside seemed almost surreal. The contrast was stark: from the cocooned, dimly-lit chamber where we danced with the winds and watched over landscapes, to the glaring brightness of day and the mundanity of the base. There's a dark humor in the juxtaposition—being able to traverse vast geographies at the touch of a joystick and then stepping out to find that your coffee has gone cold. Such is the life when you fly with the Reaper; you live in two dimensions simultaneously.

In the hours and days that followed, the mission became a source of much reflection. The flight had been a deep dive into the confluence of emotion and technology. On one hand, I felt the pride of a pilot who had successfully navigated the skies; on the other, I grappled with the ethical maze that is inherent in RPA operations. The Reaper, with its unblinking eye and lethal arsenal, epitomized the quandaries of modern warfare. It provided unmatched advantages, but it also posed questions that didn't have easy answers.

The camaraderie in the mess hall that evening was palpable. Fellow pilots and crew members, some seasoned and others fresh like me, exchanged tales from their own inaugural flights. The narratives were diverse, but a common thread ran through them all—the mix of awe and trepidation that comes with commanding such a potent tool. The jokes flew thick and fast, with many a jibe about "real pilots" versus "joystick jockeys". Military humor has always been an acquired taste, often veering into the realm of the macabre. But beneath the jesting lay a deep-seated respect for the craft and the challenges it presented.

As days transitioned into weeks and weeks into months, the patterns of RPA flights became a way of life. Each flight was unique, yet each also bore the hallmark of the Reaper's dual nature—its ability to inspire and to intimidate. But if there was one lesson that stood out, it was the importance of perspective. In a world where distances had been compressed and where actions in a dimly-lit room could have global repercussions, maintaining a clear sense of purpose was paramount.

The world of the MQ-9 Reaper is one of contrasts. It's where cutting-edge technology meets age-old dilemmas, where the boundaries of what's possible are constantly pushed, even as the ethical lines in the sand are continually redrawn. My first flight was not just a journey in the physical sense; it was an initiation into this complex tapestry. It was a foray into a realm where the sky isn't just the limit; it's the beginning.

Chapter 4: Controversy of Remote Warfare

When one contemplates the vastness and intricacies of modern warfare, they inevitably encounter the moral quandaries and ethical mazes that it presents. Among these, the use of Remotely Piloted Aircraft (RPAs) stands out as one of the most controversial and debated aspects of contemporary combat. The Reaper, with its unparalleled surveillance capability and precision-strike power, serves as the poster child of this discourse. Yet, as with all potent tools of war, its use is laced with layers of complexity that demand careful examination.

To embark on such an examination, one must first appreciate the full breadth and depth of the environment in which RPAs operate. The modern theater of war is not restricted to geographically-defined battlefields. It spans continents, delves into urban labyrinths, and stretches its tendrils into the very fabric of societies. In such a scenario, traditional means of warfare, with their collateral damage and risk to ground troops, often prove insufficient or imprudent. Herein lies the allure of the Reaper and its kin: the ability to engage without directly endangering one's own personnel and to do so with remarkable precision.

Yet, with this capability comes a slew of ethical considerations. The very detachment that RPAs provide—the absence of direct human involvement in the field—also becomes a source of moral consternation. There's an inherent dissonance in wielding immense power from thousands of miles away. The pilot, ensconced in a Ground Control Station, is both omnipotent, with a bird's-eye view of the battlefield, and impotent, shielded from the immediate consequences of their actions. This duality gives rise to a multitude of questions. Does such detachment dilute the gravity of the act of taking a life? Does it reduce war to a sanitized, almost video-game-like endeavor, stripping it of its harrowing reality?

The precision of RPAs, while an undeniable advantage, also presents its own set of challenges. With the ability to target individuals or small groups, the line between combatants and non-combatants becomes increasingly blurred. What constitutes a valid target? Is the mere association with a known adversary enough to warrant a strike? These are not merely academic musings; they are questions of life and death, with profound implications for international law and the rules of engagement.

Furthermore, the very secrecy that often shrouds RPA operations adds another layer of complexity. The lack of transparency can lead to distrust among local populations, allies, and even within the broader public of the country deploying the drones. When strikes go awry, which they inevitably do on occasion given the fog of war, the backlash is magnified manifold. The narrative then shifts from the tactical advantages of using RPAs to the human cost of remote warfare.

Yet, despite these challenges, it would be a grave oversimplification to view RPAs as mere harbingers of death from the skies. They are tools, much like any weapon in the military arsenal, and their ethical implications are a reflection of the policies guiding their use rather than inherent flaws in the technology. The debate around their deployment should, therefore, focus less on the machinery and more on the human decision-making process behind it.

As one delves deeper into the world of RPAs, it becomes clear that they are emblematic of the broader dilemmas of modern warfare. In an age where technology continually reshapes the contours of combat, the ethical challenges posed by tools like the Reaper are bound to proliferate. Addressing them requires a holistic approach, one that marries the advances in technology with a rigorous moral framework. Only then can we hope to harness the full potential of these machines while staying true to the principles that define our humanity.

In the annals of warfare, few developments have so starkly epitomized the juxtaposition of technological advancement and ethical convolution as the proliferation of Remotely Piloted Aircraft. The seemingly boundless capabilities of these aerial marvels, especially the Reaper, have thrust us into an era of unprecedented military prowess. Yet, the very traits that make them so formidable also place us on a precipice of moral quandaries, teetering between the allure of might and the shadows of ethical ambiguity.

There's a somber irony in the fact that the very name "Reaper" evokes images of the Grim Reaper, that age-old symbol of death and inevitability. For many, the Reaper drone is the modern embodiment of this ancient harbinger, swooping down from the skies to mete out judgment with a chilling precision. And like the mythical figure, it operates from a distance, its actions bearing a semblance of detachment that only deepens the moral chasm between act and consequence.

This detachment, this buffered distance from the theatre of operations, has a twofold impact on the psyche of those at the controls and those formulating strategy. On one hand, it offers a protective veneer, shielding operators from the visceral horrors of war. No longer are pilots subjected to the immediate sights, sounds, and smells of the battlefield. They are cocooned in sanitized environments, their actions mediated by screens and joysticks. Such detachment can, in theory, foster more calculated decision-making, free from the heat of the moment.

On the flip side, however, this same detachment can, and often does, engender a sense of disconnection from the profound gravity of one's actions. When the battlefield feels akin to a digital simulation, when the reverberations of one's decisions are not immediately palpable, there's a lurking danger of desensitization. It's a peculiar paradox: the more we distance ourselves from the immediacy of conflict, the closer we inch toward a potential moral abyss.

Yet, the ethical conundrums of RPAs are not solely rooted in the psychological realm. They spill over, quite prominently, into the geopolitical arena. The very stealth and efficiency of drones make them tempting tools of foreign policy, enabling states to project power without the overt footprint of traditional military interventions. Such covert operations, while tactically advantageous, are fraught with diplomatic perils. Sovereign nations bristle at perceived violations of their airspace and territorial integrity. Even when conducted with the tacit approval of host nations, RPA strikes can sow seeds of resentment among local populations, fanning the flames of radicalization. In the great game of geopolitics, the Reaper's silent wings can cast long and unpredictable shadows.

To compound matters, the cloak of secrecy that often envelops RPA operations muddies the waters of accountability. When mistakes are made, and they invariably are, the lack of transparency can exacerbate mistrust, not just among adversaries but also within the citizenry of the very nations deploying these drones. The absence of boots on the ground doesn't diminish the weight of responsibility; if anything, it accentuates the need for rigor and oversight.

In grappling with these myriad challenges, it's pivotal to remember that drones, for all their technological marvel, are but instruments.

They are the manifestations of human intent, neither inherently moral nor immoral. The onus, therefore, rests squarely on our shoulders to wield them judiciously, to marry their astounding capabilities with an unwavering commitment to ethical tenets. In the final analysis, the journey through the skies of remote warfare is as much about navigating our own moral compass as it is about charting the vast expanse of the heavens.

A Pilot's Dilemma

In the vast theater of warfare, each participant plays a pivotal role, bound by duty and honor. Yet, few roles are as drenched in paradox as that of a remotely piloted aircraft (RPA) operator. The pilot of such a machine is thrust into a situation that is as riddled with contradictions as it is steeped in responsibility. Being both detached and engaged, the pilot treads a delicate line, straddling the chasm between the visceral realities of warfare and the sterilized precision of remote technology.

Imagine, if you will, sitting in a climate-controlled room, hands gently resting on a joystick, eyes fixed on a screen that relays real-time images from thousands of miles away. The images might depict landscapes dotted with settlements, moving vehicles, and human figures going about their daily tasks. Yet, within moments, that same tranquil scene can morph into one of strategic importance, demanding crucial, often life-altering decisions from the pilot. This is the world of the RPA operator, a realm where the mundane intersects with the momentous.

At first glance, the detachment inherent in this scenario might seem a blessing. After all, isn't distance a protective shield, a buffer against the immediate traumas of war? The RPA pilot is spared the ear-shattering roar of explosions, the acrid stench of burning fuel, and the harrowing sight of destruction up close. Moreover, the physical safety afforded by this detachment can't be overstated. Far removed from the actual battlefield, the pilot is immune to the immediate threats faced by their comrades in more traditional combat roles.

Yet, this detachment is a double-edged sword. For with it comes an emotional and psychological burden that few outside the fraternity truly grasp. The pilot, in their remote sanctuary, might be shielded from immediate physical harm, but they are far from impervious to the emotional repercussions of their actions. Every push of a button, every calculated move has palpable consequences. And therein lies the crux of the dilemma: how does one reconcile the sterile, almost video game-like interface with the profound, life-and-death implications of each decision?

Moreover, this engagement is not just limited to the immediate tactical scenario unfolding on the screen. The pilot, though distanced, remains deeply embedded in the broader tapestry of the mission. They are privy to intelligence briefings, aware of the strategic importance of their targets, and cognizant of the potential ramifications of each strike. This awareness, far from being a mere backdrop, is a constant companion, shaping each decision, coloring each judgment.

This curious state of being both removed and yet profoundly connected fosters its own brand of stress, a unique strain of combat fatigue. Traditional combatants often speak of the 'fog of war,' that chaotic maelstrom where information is scarce, and decisions are driven by instinct as much as by training. For the RPA pilot, this fog takes on a different hue. It's not the lack of information but its abundance, the constant deluge of data, that can be overwhelming. Parsing this information, sifting the relevant from the redundant, all the while being acutely aware of the clock ticking down, requires a mental agility that is as draining as it is crucial.

Dark humor, a staple in many high-pressure professions, finds its way into the lexicon of RPA operators. Phrases like "playing God from the comfort of one's chair" or "delivering democracy from a distance" are bandied about with a mix of cynicism and camaraderie. Yet, beneath the veneer of these jests lies a profound truth, a reflection of the weighty responsibilities shouldered by these pilots.

In the final reckoning, the role of the RPA pilot, with its blend of detachment and engagement, stands as a testament to the evolving nature of warfare. It underscores the adaptability demanded of modern warriors; the mental fortitude required to navigate the intricacies of remote combat. As the contours of warfare continue to shift, as technology further permeates the battlefield, the experiences of these pilots will serve as both cautionary tales and guiding beacons, illuminating the path forward in an ever-changing landscape.

Chapter 5: Missions and Operations

High-Profile Surveillance Missions

Within the intricate tapestry of modern warfare and intelligence-gathering, high-profile surveillance missions, carried out by remotely piloted aircraft (RPAs), have carved a niche for themselves, showcasing a blend of technological prowess and strategic acumen. The intricate dance of tracking, identifying, and often, watching high-value targets unfolds not on the ground but thousands of feet above, orchestrated by pilots operating from the sanctuary of secure bases, often continents away.

At the heart of these missions lies the quest for intelligence, the gathering of crucial pieces of information that could swing the balance in favor of national security interests. The aim is straightforward: to observe, to record, and to understand. Yet, the intricacies involved in accomplishing this goal are anything but simple. The missions often entail surveilling individuals or locations deemed of significant interest due to their potential threat, their intelligence value, or their strategic importance in the larger geopolitical chessboard.

Now, picture this: a barren landscape, punctuated sporadically by mud-brick houses and winding roads. A vehicle, nondescript at first glance, winds its way through this setting. To the casual observer, it's just another car on just another road. But to the trained eyes of an RPA operator, that vehicle could be the linchpin in a much larger narrative. Maybe it's transporting a high-value individual, perhaps it's ferrying crucial intelligence, or it could even be on its way to a rendezvous that could have profound strategic implications. The task of the RPA, and by extension, its operator, is to tease out the story from the mundane, to find the signal in the noise.

High-profile surveillance missions are not just about collecting data; they are about collecting the right kind of data. The skies, after all, are filled with a plethora of signals. Radios chatter, mobile phones buzz, and satellite communications crisscross the atmosphere. Amidst this cacophony, the RPA must discern the voices that matter, the signals that carry weight. This entails not just technical prowess but also an understanding of the human element. The rhythms of daily life, the ebb and flow of routines, all offer clues. A break in a pattern, a deviation from the norm, could be the harbinger of something significant.

In executing these missions, RPAs have been instrumental in painting a clearer picture of the operational landscape. Their eyes in the sky have tracked the movements of militant leaders, observed the congregations of potential adversaries, and provided real-time intelligence to ground forces, thereby altering the course of operations. Their ability to loiter, to stay on station for extended periods, offers a persistence that few other platforms can match. This persistence, combined with their stealthy profile, makes them invaluable assets in the realm of high-profile surveillance.

Yet, it's essential to acknowledge the challenges inherent in such operations. The very nature of these missions, focusing on high-profile targets, means they are fraught with risk. Adversaries are often aware that they might be under observation, leading them to adopt countermeasures. From using human shields to employing electronic jamming techniques, targets employ a range of tactics to thwart surveillance efforts. Furthermore, the ethical implications of prolonged surveillance, especially in regions where the distinction between combatants and non-combatants is blurred, add another layer of complexity to these operations.

As technology continues to evolve, so too does the nature of high-profile surveillance missions. Advancements in signal processing, machine learning, and artificial intelligence promise to further refine the data collection and analysis process. However, at the heart of these missions remains the human element – the RPA operator, who must sift through mountains of data, relying on intuition as much as on technology, to piece together the puzzle.

High-profile surveillance missions encapsulate the challenges and opportunities of modern warfare. They meld cutting-edge technology with age-old tactics, shining a light on the shadowy corners of the geopolitical landscape. As the world becomes ever more interconnected, and as threats continue to evolve, the role of RPAs in these missions is poised to grow, underscoring their significance in the broader schema of defense and intelligence operations.

Of all the missions I've undertaken in my tenure as an RPA pilot, the surveillance ops often stand out as the most intense, in a cerebral sort of way. No missiles, no direct engagements, just hours of watching, analyzing, and reporting. But the stakes? They're sky-high. One such high-profile surveillance mission, codenamed "Operation Gilded Cage," remains a testament to the crucial role RPAs play in the grand chessboard of geopolitics.

It started with a tip. A foreign intelligence agency believed that an international arms dealer, known to us as "The Merchant," was peddling stolen nuclear technology. This wasn't your run-of-the-mill dealer, either. "The Merchant" was a ghost, never seen, but whose fingerprints were on illicit deals spanning continents. Intelligence suggested that a meeting was set to occur in a luxurious estate off the coast of the Black Sea, where a transaction involving stolen nuclear blueprints was to take place.

"Operation Gilded Cage" had us on the edge right from the get-go. The location was tricky. The estate was surrounded by advanced anti-air systems, making it near suicidal for manned aircraft to approach. However, our MQ-9 Reaper, equipped with state-of-the-art stealth tech and electronic countermeasures, was tasked with the near-impossible job of hovering over this hornet's nest and streaming back every bit of detail.

The day of the mission, the drone's camera feed was not just beamed to us but also to a makeshift situation room in Washington, where a cabal of high-ranking officials, including the President, would watch events unfold in real-time.

As the RPA soared over the moonlit waters of the Black Sea, I recall my co-pilot, Lt. Ramirez, humorously musing, "Ever think about how many James Bond movies we're about to outdo?" But beneath the levity lay a tension you could cut with a knife.

The feed from the RPA soon presented us with a panorama of the estate – sprawling lawns, a palatial mansion, helipads, and docks with yachts that cost more than a small country's GDP. The infrared picked up numerous heat signatures, indicating heavy security. But where was "The Merchant"?

Hours rolled by, with every flicker of movement, every car that entered, every shadowy figure that emerged being documented, timestamped, and analyzed. Then, just as the first rays of dawn began to emerge, a yacht unlike any other we'd seen before docked at the private pier. Its very appearance screamed discretion and opulence. And there he was. "The Merchant," surrounded by an entourage, disembarked.

In the tense hours that followed, our RPA chronicled every move. We watched as crates, presumably carrying the illicit materials, were offloaded and transferred to an underground facility within the estate. Every individual, every license plate, every boat that approached was cataloged.

Yet, amid this clandestine ballet, one scene remains etched in memory. As "The Merchant" and his potential buyers raised a toast on the balcony, likely celebrating their nefarious deal, Ramirez dryly commented, "Cheers to us, too, for the front-row seats to this blockbuster."

The mission's climax arrived when the gathered intel provided the catalyst for a multinational covert operation a few days later, resulting in the apprehension of "The Merchant" and the seizure of the stolen nuclear technology.

"Operation Gilded Cage" didn't just underscore the technical prowess of RPAs. It spotlighted the patience, the meticulousness, and the immense responsibility shouldered by RPA operators. We weren't just pilots; we were silent guardians, unseen sentinels in the vast expanses of the sky, ensuring that the world below remained just a bit safer from shadows that sought to unleash chaos.

Coordinating with Ground Forces

In the evolving domain of contemporary warfare, the synchronization between aerial capabilities—embodied most notably by remotely piloted aircraft (RPAs)—and ground forces stands out as a paramount factor in ensuring operational success. This intricate ballet of coordination is an exercise in precision, timing, and mutual trust. For while the skies may offer a vantage point unparalleled, it's the ground where objectives are secured, territories are held, and the tangible outcomes of military engagements are realized. The interplay between these two dimensions of warfare, the aerial and the terrestrial, therefore, demands a scrutiny of considerable depth.

Now, one must first appreciate the unique perspective that RPAs bring to the theater of operations. Hovering silently thousands of feet in the air, these machines are the proverbial eyes in the sky, offering a bird's eye view of the unfolding situation on the ground. They can track enemy movements, relay real-time intelligence, and even engage hostile targets if armed. Yet, for all their technological sophistication, RPAs are tools—albeit advanced ones—and their efficacy hinges on the seamless integration of their capabilities with the strategies and tactics of the ground forces they support.

Imagine, if you will, a convoy of ground troops advancing through challenging terrain, perhaps an urban setting with its maze of alleyways or a rugged mountainous region. The inherent vulnerabilities in such situations are palpable: ambushes, IEDs, or even snipers. Here, the RPA doesn't merely serve as a watchful guardian from above but becomes an extension of the convoy itself. Through the data relayed by the RPA, the ground force commander can make informed decisions, preemptively adjusting the convoy's route to avoid threats, or even calling in reinforcements should the need arise.

However, such effective coordination is not spontaneously birthed. It's the culmination of rigorous training, extensive planning, and a profound understanding of both the capabilities of the RPA and the needs of the ground forces. Communication channels must be robust, encrypted, and free from latency. The RPA operators need to be fluent in the language and protocols of ground warfare, understanding the nuances of infantry tactics, armored maneuvers, and the often fluid dynamics of combat zones. On the flip side, ground force commanders must be adept at rapidly processing aerial intelligence, translating that data into actionable insights for their units.

The realm of joint operations further accentuates the importance of this coordination. In scenarios where multiple nation-states ally their forces, the complexities are magnified. Here, RPAs might be operated by one nation, supporting the ground forces of another, navigating the intricate tapestries of differing military doctrines, operational terminologies, and even variations in technological interfaces. Such situations necessitate not only bilateral trust but also an almost symphonic level of harmony in joint operations strategy.

Yet, it would be remiss to discuss the coordination between RPAs and ground forces without addressing the occasional discord that arises. Sometimes, the detachment of an RPA operator, safely ensconced miles away, can lead to a disconnect with the immediate exigencies faced by ground troops. The RPA's camera might relay crisp images, but it cannot convey the cacophony of a firefight, the dust and smoke, or the visceral tension of imminent danger. This underscores the need for cultivating a deep sense of empathy and trust. The ground troops must believe in the watchful vigilance of their eye in the sky, and the RPA operators must always prioritize the safety and objectives of their comrades on the ground.

In reflecting upon these dynamics, it becomes abundantly clear that the future of modern warfare lies in an ever-tightening nexus between air and land capabilities. As technologies advance, bringing forth even more sophisticated RPAs and ground equipment, the onus will be on the human elements to refine their coordination, to train harder, and to foster an ethos of mutual respect and understanding.

In the grand tapestry of military operations, the relationship between RPAs and ground forces can be likened to the symbiosis in nature. Each entity, while powerful in its own right, realizes its full potential only when seamlessly integrated with the other. This integration, rooted in trust, communication, and mutual respect, promises not only enhanced operational outcomes but also the safeguarding of lives, ensuring that the brave men and women in the field are always backed by the unblinking gaze of their guardians in the skies.

A few years into my tenure as an RPA pilot, there was a particular mission that still stands out vividly in my memory, both for its intense challenges and the seamless coordination it necessitated with our ground troops. Codenamed "Operation Midnight Falcon," the mission epitomized the intricate ballet between our eyes in the sky and the boots on the ground.

It began with intelligence suggesting that a high-value target, an insurgent leader notorious for his strategic acumen and elusive nature, was convening a meeting with his lieutenants in a remote village nestled amidst the rugged mountains of northern Afghanistan. The opportunity to incapacitate this linchpin in the enemy's command structure was invaluable. However, the terrain and the innocuous nature of the village posed significant challenges. A direct assault risked civilian casualties and might also allow the target to escape, given his track record of evading capture.

Our initial role was reconnaissance. For days, the RPA I operated surveilled the village, mapping out its narrow lanes, identifying potential escape routes, and locating the exact compound where the meeting was expected to happen. During this phase, we maintained a constant line of communication with the ground force commander, Captain Alvarez, and his elite strike team, prepping for a surgical raid.

One evening, as the shadows lengthened and the amber hue of the setting sun blanketed the village, our RPA's infrared sensors picked up a convoy of vehicles approaching the identified compound. The heat signatures corresponded with the intelligence we had: a dozen armed guards and a few individuals who could very well be our high-value targets.

Captain Alvarez and his team, already in a concealed position on a ridge overlooking the village, were immediately informed. But the challenge was clear: the approach to the compound was open ground, leaving the team exposed and vulnerable. To make matters more intricate, children were playing in the streets, and the evening call to prayer meant more civilians would be about.

Time was of the essence, but rushing in blindly was not an option. My RPA, now hovering at an altitude to minimize noise yet close enough to provide granular details, began feeding Alvarez real-time data. We spotted a herd of goats on the eastern side, creating a temporary visual barrier against one of the watchtowers. A few villagers were congregating around a local well to the north, drawing the attention of a couple of guards.

Recognizing this, Alvarez made a decision that showcased the epitome of trust between ground forces and RPA operators. He asked us to simulate a minor equipment malfunction on the RPA, causing it to drop altitude briefly and then correct itself—essentially, a controlled feint. As anticipated, this drew the attention of several guards, their eyes scanning the skies, trying to locate this mechanical bird that had dared come so close.

Seizing the momentary diversion, Alvarez's team moved swiftly, using the goats as cover, and entered an adjoining compound. Here's where the dark humor came in. Over the comms, Alvarez quipped, "Bet they never taught you in flight school that your multi-million-dollar tech would play second fiddle to a herd of goats!"

From that point onward, it was a masterclass in coordination. The RPA tracked guard movements, pinpointing their locations for Alvarez's team. Through whispered communications and the relayed visuals from our drone, the strike team moved from shadow to shadow, compound to compound. Their approach was methodical, ensuring minimal disturbance and zero civilian harm.

The culmination came when they breached the main compound. With a combination of flashbangs and swift room-clearing procedures, the operation was a success. The high-value target, alongside his lieutenants, was apprehended with no casualties on either side.

Back at base, amidst the congratulations and debriefings, Alvarez approached me. With a firm handshake and a wry smile, he said, "You know, up there in the skies, you might not hear the bullets or feel the dust. But today, you were right there with us in every room, every corner. That's some team play."

That mission was more than just an operational success; it underscored the deep symbiotic relationship between RPA operators and ground forces. It was a testament to trust, mutual respect, and the collective goal of achieving objectives with precision and conscience. It's missions like "Operation Midnight Falcon" that validate the profound interconnectedness of modern warfare, showcasing that whether in the skies or on the ground, we fight as one.

Strike Operations: Precision and Challenges

When it comes to military affairs, few operations elicit as much intrigue, debate, and downright awe as strike operations, especially those conducted from the cold, unblinking eye of an RPA, the Remotely Piloted Aircraft. These operations, with their dizzying blend of technology, strategy, and, inevitably, the human element, represent both the pinnacle of military precision and the quagmire of ethical challenges.

To many, the very idea of a strike operation executed from thousands of miles away, often from the comfort of a well-conditioned room, seems the stuff of science fiction. Yet, in today's technologically-driven theaters of war, it is a reality that military personnel, policymakers, and indeed, the global citizen, grapple with daily. A strike operation, by its nature, seeks to deliver decisive force upon a target. It aims to disrupt, degrade, or, in many cases, completely eliminate a perceived threat. When executed from an RPA, this action combines the meticulousness of surveillance with the suddenness of force application.

Take, for instance, the MQ-9 Reaper, which over the years, has earned both accolades for its precision and scrutiny for the very detached nature of its operations. Outfitted with an array of Hellfire missiles and laser-guided bombs, the Reaper stands as a testament to the marvels of military engineering. With a single drone, commanders have at their disposal an asset that can linger over battlefields for hours, identify high-value targets with impeccable accuracy, and, when the command is given, unleash firepower that can change the tide of a conflict.

Yet, herein lies one of the central dilemmas of RPA-driven strike operations. The very distance, both physical and emotional, between the pilot and the target zone. Traditionally, pilots have had to contend with the immediate ramifications of their actions. The sounds, the vibrations, the very tangible consequences of dropping ordnance. But with an RPA, one could theoretically execute a strike operation during one's work shift and be back home for a family dinner mere hours later. This dichotomy, where war is waged in one instant and domestic normalcy resumes in the next, represents one of the most profound shifts in the nature of warfare. The soldier is no longer "away at war." Instead, war is something one "commutes to."

The precision of RPA-driven strikes cannot be understated. With advancements in imaging technology, target recognition software, and real-time data analytics, RPAs have minimized one of the most haunting aspects of warfare: collateral damage. Today's drones can differentiate between combatants and civilians, between a threat and an innocent, with a level of detail that is, frankly, astounding. They can execute a strike with surgical precision, ensuring that the intended target, and only the intended target, faces the wrath of the payload.

However, this precision doesn't automatically absolve the complexities that arise. Just because a drone can strike accurately doesn't always mean it should. The human element, the final decision-making process, remains fraught with ethical considerations. What if the intelligence is wrong? What if the target, while a combatant, is in a location that poses moral challenges, such as a hospital or a school? What about the psychological toll on the operator, who, despite the physical distance, must live with the knowledge and the visuals of the aftermath?

Moreover, while technology has advanced, it is not infallible. There are instances where equipment malfunctions, where signals are lost, or where the sheer unpredictability of the ground situation results in unintended consequences. In such scenarios, the backlash, both locally and internationally, can be significant.

Furthermore, the legality of these strikes, especially those conducted outside the traditional theaters of war, raises significant questions. Sovereignty, international law, the rights of individuals versus state security—these are all dimensions that come to the fore when discussing RPA strikes.

To say that RPA-driven strike operations have transformed the face of modern warfare would be an understatement. They offer nations the ability to project power without significant footprints, to deter adversaries, and to eliminate threats with a level of accuracy previously unimaginable. Yet, they also usher in a plethora of challenges, ranging from the ethical to the legal, from the psychological to the strategic.

In navigating this brave new world of warfare, it becomes essential to remember that technology, no matter how advanced, is only a tool. The decisions, the repercussions, and the moral weight of using this tool rest, as they always have, on the frail shoulders of humanity.

The digital landscape of modern warfare, as portrayed through the lens of RPAs, is filled with tales that oscillate between the spectrums of valor and introspection, success and unforeseen complications. Here, I recall a few missions that encapsulate the essence of what it means to be at the helm of such a potent instrument of war.

Operation Silent Mirage

The day started like any other. The digital feed showed a desolate landscape dotted with the occasional scrub and structures. Our mission was to track a high-profile target, a leader in an extremist faction responsible for multiple bombings across the region. Intelligence had pinpointed his location to a small hamlet near the foothills.

Hours went by as we circled above, the MQ-9 Reaper's unyielding gaze constantly scanning, always watching. The anticipation was palpable, but the weight of responsibility was even more so. A confirmed sighting came in mid-afternoon. There he was, stepping out of a vehicle, surrounded by bodyguards.

Given the precise nature of our technology and the clear line of sight, it would have been easy to engage right then. But the vicinity bore the marks of civilian life—children playing, women drawing water from a well. The dilemma was stark. While we had a visual on a prime target, a single miscalculation could result in innocent lives lost.

Our patience paid off. As night approached, our target moved to a more secluded location. After cross-checking with multiple intel sources and ensuring minimal collateral, the decision was made. The Reaper's Hellfire missile found its mark, and a key threat was neutralized. The operation was deemed a success, but the hours of waiting, the moral dilemmas faced, and the precision required left an indelible mark on all involved.

Nightfall Hunt

There are times in the annals of RPA piloting when you're not just battling the enemy on the ground, but also the elements. One such mission had us tracking an arms shipment in a region notorious for its sudden and fierce sandstorms.

Intel suggested that a convoy carrying advanced weaponry would move under the cover of night. The intention was clear: use the vast desert and the darkness as cover. They probably didn't reckon they'd be up against an RPA with advanced thermal imaging and radar capabilities.

Yet, nature threw a curveball. A massive sandstorm was brewing. While our RPA could navigate above it, the reduced visibility meant tracking the convoy would be a challenge. Through sheer skill, our ground team recalibrated the sensors to detect disturbances in the storm patterns. Essentially, we were not looking for the convoy itself, but its interaction with the environment.

Hours into the mission, a distinct pattern emerged—a trail of disturbed sand and wind, painting a spectral image of the convoy below. Utilizing this data, we were able to predict its path and, once in a suitable location, launch a precise strike that neutralized the threat. It was a testament not just to the technology but to the innovation and adaptability of the human minds behind it.

Whispers in the Wind

In some missions, the impact isn't just about the immediate strike but the long-term repercussions it brings about. We were tasked with taking out a communications hub that was being used by hostile forces to coordinate attacks across multiple fronts. The catch? It was located in a densely populated urban setting.

Every building, every alley was a potential hiding spot, and more importantly, each held the risk of civilian casualties. Our drone circled for days, mapping out patterns, understanding routines. We observed the frequent movements of guards, the shielding mechanisms, and even the local kids playing soccer in the evenings.

After thorough surveillance, a pattern emerged. There was a small window in the early morning hours when guard shifts changed, and the immediate vicinity had the least civilian presence. The strike was planned for then. The missile was released, and the hub was destroyed without any collateral damage. But beyond the immediate success, the subsequent intel revealed that the strike had a cascading effect, severely crippling coordinated attacks for months.

These missions, while distinct in their objectives, underscore the manifold complexities of RPA-driven strike operations. They are a testament to the potent combination of cutting-edge technology and the unyielding human spirit. They highlight the precision that drones bring to the modern battlefield, but also the myriad of ethical, tactical, and environmental challenges that pilots and their teams must navigate. Every mission is a story, and every story adds a new facet to the ever-evolving narrative of warfare in the digital age.

Chapter 6: The Human Touch in Remote Flying

Developing a Bond with the Machine

In an age dominated by technological advancements, where screens become interfaces for human connection and algorithms predict our next move, it might seem peculiar to the uninitiated to speak of a bond, an emotional connection, between a pilot and their remotely piloted aircraft. After all, these unmanned vehicles, steered from thousands of miles away, could easily be considered cold, mechanical tools—functional and efficient, but devoid of soul. Yet, as any pilot will passionately attest, these machines are so much more than the sum of their metal parts and computer codes. The relationship is intricate, deep-rooted, and immensely personal, and it's crucial to understand this bond to appreciate the psychological and emotional world of an RPA pilot.

One of the core principles of aviation, which any pilot from any era will acknowledge, is the profound connection between aviator and aircraft. When a pilot steps into a traditional cockpit, they are not merely operating an aircraft; they are merging with it, becoming a part of a larger entity that dances with the winds and defies the very laws of gravity. The pilot feels every vibration, every hum, every pulse of the machine, and responds with intuition as much as skill. It is a relationship built on mutual trust. In the world of RPAs, this bond transcends the physical. It becomes an interplay of trust, not with tangible metal and gears, but with pixels, data feeds, and radio waves.

In my early days of remote piloting, the sensation was disorienting. Sitting in a ground control station, surrounded by monitors and joysticks, I felt a distinct detachment from the MQ-9 Reaper that I was operating. There was no vibration underfoot, no sensation of speed or altitude, and no roar of engines. But, over time, something profound occurred. I began to realize that the Reaper and I were forging a new kind of bond. Just as a musician finds an extension of their soul in their instrument or a painter in their brush, I was discovering a kindred spirit in this technological marvel.

The many hours spent guiding the drone over varied terrains and through countless missions allowed me to develop a rhythm with the machine. I could predict its responses, understand its quirks, and, in a strange way, sense its 'mood'. When latency issues arose or when a particular sensor acted up, it felt akin to a trusted horse limping or a seasoned guitar going slightly out of tune. It wasn't a malfunction; it was a communication. The machine was 'speaking', and it was my job, my duty, to listen and understand.

There were lighter moments too, born from the camaraderie among pilots. We would often joke about our drones having personalities. One might be labeled the 'stubborn old mule' for its persistent minor technical hitches, while another might be the 'eager rookie', always responsive, always raring to go. These anthropomorphic tendencies were more than just whimsical banter. They were indicative of the deep-seated human need to connect, to find resonance, even in the most unexpected of places.

This bond, while emotionally gratifying, also has a crucial operational aspect. A pilot deeply attuned to their RPA can operate it more efficiently, respond to anomalies more quickly, and make judgment calls with heightened accuracy. It becomes less about controlling and more about collaborating. It's a dance, a partnership, where both entities, man and machine, are synchronizing their strengths to achieve a collective objective.

However, it's also essential to acknowledge the unique challenges this bond can present. In situations where the drone is compromised or lost, the sense of loss can be deeply personal. It's not just equipment that's gone; it's a comrade. The emotional toll can be significant and is a testament to the depth of the connection that pilots forge with their machines.

In the vast, intricate tapestry of modern warfare, where drones are becoming the threads weaving together strategies and missions, the bond between a pilot and their RPA stands as a poignant reminder of the human essence that persists amidst the mechanical and the digital. It underscores the truth that at the heart of every technological marvel is a human spirit, guiding it, understanding it, and, most importantly, connecting with it. The world of RPAs, thus, is not just a realm of codes and algorithms; it's a space where human emotions, instincts, and bonds find new avenues of expression and resonance. It's where the heart meets the machine.

It might come as a surprise to many that despite the physical distance and the layers of technology between the pilot and the RPA, a sense of kinship develops. However, this affinity is an age-old phenomenon rooted in the chronicles of human history. Throughout the annals of time, mankind has showcased an innate ability to imbue soulless entities with personality, character, and essence, from ancient mariners naming their vessels to the car enthusiasts of today speaking fondly of their 'rides'. This propensity to personify is not a manifestation of delusion, but rather a profound testimony to the human ability to seek connection in all facets of existence.

With each mission I embarked upon with my trusty MQ-9 Reaper, I began to recognize this connection even more. The drone was not just an assemblage of sensors, wires, and codes. It was an entity with which I had shared countless hours, experienced a multitude of emotions ranging from trepidation to exhilaration, and faced moments that questioned the very essence of my professional ethos. Each altitude adjustment, each camera pan, each minor calibration became an intricate step in the elaborate ballet that we performed together. The Reaper and I were, in those moments of intense concentration and flawless operation, extensions of one another.

There was this one instance, in particular, I remember vividly. The mission parameters had been straightforward - a simple surveillance over an area with suspected insurgent activity. But as the drone soared over the rugged terrains, the weather turned capricious. A storm was brewing, and the satellite links became spotty. For a few heart-stopping moments, the connection was lost. I sat there, staring at the blank screens, the silence in the control room echoing the tumult in my mind. When the link was finally re-established, the relief I felt was not just because the mission could continue, but because my distant partner in the skies was 'safe'. It felt as if a friend had been momentarily lost in a crowded place, only to be found again.

Further adding complexity to the relationship is the ever-present background hum of ethical considerations. Each time the Reaper and I embarked on a mission, there was the weighty knowledge that the outcomes were not just pixels on a screen but real, tangible events with profound consequences. The drone, despite its cutting-edge technology, did not possess moral judgment, compassion, or ethical grounding. Those were solely mine to grapple with, and in moments of solitude, I often found myself reflecting on the ramifications of our combined actions.

The digital age often stands accused of dehumanizing experiences, of creating distances, of turning genuine emotions into mere emoticons on screens. However, the bond between an RPA pilot and their machine offers a different narrative. It showcases that even in the heart of this digital revolution, humans have an uncanny ability to seek, find, and nurture connections. This bond is not born out of mere familiarity but from shared experiences, from moments of tension and relief, from the silent understanding that even though one entity is made of flesh and blood and the other of metal and circuits, they are, in those mission moments, parts of a harmonious whole.

Thus, the human touch in remote flying is not an oxymoron. It's a testament to the adaptability of human emotions and the indomitable spirit of connection that refuses to be confined by geographical distances or technological interfaces. It reminds us that in the intricate dance of progress, humanity remains the lead, guiding and being guided, connecting and being connected, and finding soulful symphonies even in the most unexpected places.

The Emotions of Flying an RPA

When many think of emotions and flying, they may immediately conjure up images of a pilot in a cockpit, feeling the rush of the wind, the vibrations of the engines, and the adrenaline of takeoff. They might imagine the visceral feelings of elation when breaking through clouds, or the tension of landing in adverse conditions. But in the realm of Remotely Piloted Aircrafts (RPAs), the emotional landscape, though differently textured, is no less varied or intense.

At first glance, one might assume that piloting an RPA, physically removed from the actual machine, might be a sterile, emotionless task — something akin to playing a video game. But this notion is far from reality. The act of controlling an RPA, particularly in mission-critical scenarios, carries with it a tapestry of emotions that range from intense concentration to profound introspection, from soaring pride to deep-seated ethical dilemmas.

Consider, for a moment, the initial sensation of disconnection. Here you are, seated in a control room, potentially thousands of miles away from the RPA you are maneuvering. The very act of flying without being 'in' the aircraft can be disorienting. The typical, tangible feedback — the G-forces on ascent or the slight jolt of turbulence — are notably absent. Instead, they're replaced by a profound reliance on data streams, visual feeds, and instrumentation readings. This detachment can sometimes lead to a sense of unreality, where the consequences of one's actions might not immediately register.

But this distance doesn't diminish the weight of responsibility. If anything, it amplifies it. Every mission carries with it the knowledge that the RPA, with its sophisticated equipment, is a multi-million-dollar asset. More importantly, its operations, especially in conflict zones, have real-world consequences. A surveillance operation might be gathering intelligence that will inform critical decisions on the ground. A strike operation, even more gravely, could result in the loss of life. This burden of duty, combined with the physical detachment, creates a unique emotional cocktail where clinical precision meets profound contemplation.

There's also the paradox of solitude. An RPA pilot, during operations, is often isolated in their control booth. Yet, they're in continuous communication with a team, be it intelligence officers, military strategists, or fellow pilots. This duality, of being alone yet surrounded, can lead to feelings of both empowerment and loneliness. Every decision made in that booth can have ramifications, and while there's a team for support, the immediacy of the decisions often rests on the pilot's shoulders.

Then comes the uncharted territory of ethics. Traditional pilots, when in combat scenarios, have the immediate threat of personal harm. There's an inherent balance — they are both the deliverers and potential recipients of force. With RPAs, this dynamic shifts dramatically. The pilot is safe, often continents away from any direct threat. Yet, they hold in their hands the power to deploy lethal force. This can lead to a complex emotional maelstrom — pride in one's skills, the satisfaction of a mission accomplished, juxtaposed with the weighty knowledge of the power they wield and its consequences. Pilots can find themselves wrestling with questions that philosophers have debated for millennia about the nature of war, duty, and morality.

Furthermore, there's an emotional toll that comes from the nature of RPA missions. Surveillance operations often require observing targets for extended durations. This can lead to an uncomfortable familiarity with the subject — seeing them in their daily routines, understanding their habits, and then, if the mission calls for it, striking.

This prolonged engagement creates a connection that traditional pilots, dropping munitions from altitudes, rarely experience. The intimate knowledge of a target's life, followed by the potential act of ending it, can be an emotionally jarring experience.

While the world of RPA piloting might seem cold and distant to those on the outside, it is a cauldron of emotions, challenges, and soul-searching moments. As the world moves further into the age of remote warfare, understanding, acknowledging, and addressing these emotional landscapes will be crucial. For behind every drone's operation, behind every pixelated image on a control screen, is a human being, with all the depth, complexity, and emotion that entails.

Chapter 7: Risks and Challenges

Dealing with Malfunctions

In the wide-ranging discourse on Remotely Piloted Aircrafts (RPAs), there exists an oft-touted belief that these machines, by virtue of their advanced technological foundations, are infallible. The concept that a machine, curated and refined over years of dedicated research, would exhibit vulnerabilities seems almost anathema to those who stand on the outside looking in. However, like all man-made instruments, RPAs are not immune to malfunctions. These malfunctions, while occurring in the high-altitude, vast expanse of the skies, bring forth a set of challenges and risks that are both tangible and deeply disconcerting.

When one broaches the subject of malfunctions in traditional aircraft, the physical danger to the pilot and crew is palpable. The threat of plummeting altitudes, loss of control, and the very real possibility of a fatal crash, strikes fear into even the most stolid heart. But in the world of RPAs, the absence of on-board human life often leads to a misleading belief that malfunctions are less dangerous, less consequential. This, unfortunately, is a misguided notion. The lack of immediate human jeopardy does not diminish the breadth or depth of risks associated with RPA malfunctions.

At the outset, one must recognize the significant financial implications. RPAs, especially the more advanced models, represent significant investments. Their technological components are both intricate and costly. A malfunction leading to the loss of an RPA can result in the forfeiture of millions of dollars. But, as anyone deeply entrenched in the world of aerial warfare would argue, the fiscal aspect, though considerable, is far from being the most pressing concern.

The data that an RPA collects is of paramount importance. In an era where information is both weapon and shield, the loss of data, due to malfunction, can be strategically debilitating. The intelligence gathered, the patterns observed, and the targets identified, all form a mosaic of information that plays a pivotal role in shaping decisions on the ground. A malfunction that compromises this data integrity or leads to its loss can have ramifications that ripple across theaters of operation.

Then there is the undeniable concern of where a malfunctioning RPA might end up. While these aircraft are designed to default to safety protocols in case of a system failure, such measures are not always foolproof. A malfunction could result in an RPA going off-course, potentially entering hostile or neutral territories. This not only poses the risk of the technology falling into adversarial hands but also carries the weighty implications of diplomatic incidents, potential escalations, or breaches of international law.

Let's delve deeper into the nature of these malfunctions. Technological glitches can range from minor software bugs to critical hardware failures. A minor glitch in the RPA's camera system might impair vision, whereas a more severe malfunction in its navigation system might render the aircraft directionless. In some unfortunate instances, there might be a complete loss of control link between the pilot and the RPA. These moments, where the aircraft becomes a rogue entity, are among the most stressful and challenging for RPA operators.

Compounding the tangible risks is the emotional and psychological toll on the pilots. Imagine, for a moment, the sensation of watching helplessly as a multi-million-dollar asset, which you were responsible for, veers off course, with no way of regaining control. The feeling of helplessness, combined with the anticipation of potential repercussions, can be overwhelming. Such incidents, over time, can lead to a reluctance in pilots to trust the very technology they operate, causing hesitation and second-guessing.

Moreover, the realm of cyber warfare has added another layer of vulnerability. Sophisticated adversaries continually seek to exploit technological loopholes, aiming to hack or disrupt RPA operations. An

RPA, taken over by hostile forces through cyber intrusion, becomes not just a lost asset but a potential weapon turned against its owners.

The world of RPAs, while bringing forth a myriad of advantages, is not without its set of risks and challenges. Malfunctions, both minor and catastrophic, serve as a sobering reminder of the inherent vulnerabilities of relying heavily on technology. As we venture deeper into this age of remote warfare, it becomes imperative to continually refine, review, and reinforce the technological bulwarks that keep these machines running. For in the vast, unforgiving theater of aerial warfare, there is little room for error.

The Pressure of Making Crucial Decisions

Navigating the labyrinthine world of Remotely Piloted Aircrafts (RPAs) is not merely a technological endeavor but also a profoundly human one. The intersection of man and machine presents a myriad of challenges, many of which are not immediately discernible to the casual observer. One of the most pressing and often under-discussed facets of this dynamic is the immense pressure that pilots face when making crucial decisions. It's a realm where microseconds can shape destinies, and the weight of these choices can be both immediate and far-reaching.

When we envisage the role of an RPA pilot, there's often a tendency to focus on the technical aspects of the job. The piloting skills, the understanding of the equipment, the proficiency in handling complex machinery from miles away—these are undoubtedly critical components of the job description. However, just as crucial, if not more so, is the pilot's ability to make split-second decisions that can have consequences ranging from the strategic to the profoundly personal.

Consider, for instance, the act of surveillance. From the vantage point of an RPA, the world below unfolds in a tapestry of details. Every moving figure, every vehicle, every puff of smoke becomes a data point. But intertwined with this data is the necessity to interpret, to analyze, and to decide. Is that figure a combatant or a civilian? Is that vehicle transporting arms or is it merely a farmer's truck? The pressure of making these determinations, knowing that a wrong assessment can result in civilian casualties or a missed target, is immense. Every pixel displayed on the pilot's screen is a potential decision point, and each choice carries a weight that can sometimes be unbearable.

Beyond the immediate operational decisions lies a broader spectrum of strategic choices. The data gathered by an RPA doesn't exist in a vacuum. It forms part of a larger narrative—a narrative that shapes policy decisions, informs military strategy, and influences diplomatic dialogues. An RPA pilot, while ostensibly removed from the theater of ground operations, plays a pivotal role in shaping this narrative. The responsibility of ensuring accuracy, of verifying facts before transmitting them, and of understanding the broader implications of the data being gathered, adds another layer of pressure.

In addition, there's an ethical dimension to these decisions. The act of remote warfare, while reducing risks to personnel, also introduces a degree of detachment. The physical distance might create an illusion of impersonality, but the moral and ethical dimensions remain as potent as ever. When deciding to release a missile, the pilot isn't merely pressing a button; they are making a life and death decision. The pressure of reconciling the detachment of remote operations with the very real consequences of one's actions is a challenge that every RPA pilot grapples with.

Furthermore, the world of RPAs is not static. The rapid evolution of technology means that pilots are continually adapting to new equipment, new protocols, and new challenges. Every advancement, while enhancing capabilities, also brings forth a new set of decisions to be made. The pressure of staying updated, of undergoing constant training, and of adapting to shifting goalposts is a relentless undercurrent in the pilot's professional journey.

It's also worth noting that the weight of these decisions isn't just felt in the operational moment. The aftermath, the introspection, and the second-guessing can take a significant emotional toll. RPAs might be machines, but their operators are profoundly human. The emotional and psychological implications of their choices, especially when things don't go as planned, can linger long after a mission has concluded.

In this vast, interconnected tapestry of technology, strategy, ethics, and emotion, the RPA pilot stands at the nexus. The pressure of making crucial decisions, of balancing the micro with the macro, the immediate with the long-term, and the personal with the impersonal, is a testament to the multifaceted challenges of modern warfare. As we delve deeper into the era of remote operations, understanding and addressing these pressures becomes paramount. For at the heart of this technological marvel lies the age-old human quest for judgment, responsibility, and the reconciliation of choices made in the most challenging of circumstances.

RPAs, despite being the zenith of technological evolution in modern warfare, serve as a poignant reminder that human choices remain inextricably linked with machines. As we chart the trajectory of an RPA pilot's journey, it becomes clear that while the skies may have become more digitized, the cognitive and emotional landscapes pilots navigate have only grown more intricate and tumultuous.

An analogy often made is that of comparing RPA pilots to the players of a highly sophisticated video game. The outside observer may perceive the detachment, the screens, and the joysticks, and draw parallels. However, this oversimplification fails to capture the gravitas of the decisions pilots make daily. Unlike a video game, there's no "reset" button. The stakes are real, as are the lives impacted by each decision.

Several past missions underscore the multifaceted challenges that RPA pilots encounter. One pilot recounted a mission where intelligence suggested the presence of a high-value target within a particular building in a densely populated area. The feed from the drone clearly showed the suspect entering the building. However, the same feed also revealed children playing nearby. The window to act was narrow, but the potential for collateral damage was palpable. In the nerve-wracking minutes that followed, the pilot grappled with a moral and tactical quandary. Acting might neutralize a threat but at a possibly unacceptable cost. Abstaining might allow a dangerous individual to escape. The pilot ultimately decided not to strike, a decision that was later validated when further intelligence confirmed the presence of civilians inside the building. The target did escape, but the potential tragedy was averted.

The after-action review of this mission brought to light the nuances of such decisions. Some argued that the pilot's hesitation could have jeopardized future operations. Others lauded the restraint shown. The pilot, however, was left wrestling with the what-ifs. The emotional aftermath of such missions is often as intense, if not more so, than the operations themselves.

Another pilot narrated a different kind of pressure. While tracking a convoy suspected of carrying contraband in a conflict-ridden region, the RPA's systems began to malfunction. The visual feed became patchy, and the drone's responsiveness was compromised. Here, the decision was not just about strike or no-strike. It was about whether to continue the operation with compromised equipment, risking not just the mission but also the expensive machinery. The pilot decided to abort, prioritizing safety over the immediate mission objective. Later, it was discovered that a minor software glitch had caused the malfunction, which was rectified promptly. Still, the decision underscored the pilot's responsibility not just to the mission but also to the integrity of the equipment and the broader objectives of the campaign.

These stories, while offering a glimpse into the pilot's world, also highlight a more profound truth. The evolution of warfare, with its drones and remote capabilities, hasn't simplified the human dimension. If anything, it has added layers of complexity. The decisions RPA pilots make, while buttressed by technology, remain rooted in age-old dilemmas of warfare — the balance of risk and reward, the moral imperatives versus strategic objectives, and the ever-present shadow of unpredictability.

In this evolving landscape, the RPA pilot stands not just as a harbinger of a new era but also as a custodian of the timeless ethos of warfare. The pressure of making crucial decisions remains as enduring as ever, reminding us that while machines may change, the human soul's challenges and triumphs remain eternal.

The Psychological Impact of Remote Warfare

The rise of Remotely Piloted Aircrafts (RPAs) and the widespread adoption of drone warfare have significantly transformed the landscape of contemporary conflict. This evolution, while offering a host of tactical advantages, has also ushered in a set of unique psychological challenges for those at the controls. As warfare becomes increasingly remote, the psychological ramifications of this detachment are becoming more pronounced, and their understanding becomes crucial for both military efficacy and the well-being of operators.

At the outset, it's tempting to assume that the detachment inherent in drone warfare would serve as a buffer, insulating pilots from the traditional traumas of combat. After all, they are not physically present in the theater of operations, shielded from immediate danger and the visceral realities of war. However, this perspective, while intuitive, is overly simplistic and fails to encompass the multifaceted psychological dimensions that come into play.

One of the primary psychological challenges faced by RPA pilots is the juxtaposition of their operational environment with their day-to-day life. Unlike traditional combatants who are deployed to war zones, RPA pilots often operate from bases situated in peaceful territories, sometimes even within their home countries. This daily transition between participating in intense military operations and then returning to the mundanities of domestic life — attending parent-teacher meetings, grocery shopping, or going for a jog — can be jarring. This dual existence, fluctuating between the roles of a warrior and a civilian, can lead to cognitive dissonance and stress.

Additionally, the very nature of drone warfare accentuates the intimacy of combat. RPAs are often equipped with high-resolution cameras, allowing pilots a detailed, up-close view of their targets and the aftermath of their actions. This magnified perspective, paradoxically, can make the act of executing a mission more personal and confronting, even from thousands of miles away. Watching a target for days, getting familiar with their patterns, and then being the one to make the call can weigh heavily on the psyche.

There's also the matter of temporal elasticity in drone warfare. Traditional combat is often punctuated by adrenaline-filled moments of action, followed by periods of downtime or retreat. In contrast, RPA operations can entail long hours of surveillance, monitoring, and waiting — a continuous stretch of heightened anticipation. This prolonged state of alertness, coupled with the absence of tangible indicators of danger like the sounds and smells of a battlefield, can result in chronic stress and fatigue.

Moreover, the discourse surrounding drone warfare in popular culture and media often paints RPA pilots as mere 'button pushers', trivializing their role and the complexities they navigate. Such perceptions can lead to a sense of professional isolation, where pilots feel their experiences and challenges are misunderstood or diminished by both their civilian peers and, at times, their comrades in traditional combat roles.

Lastly, there's the ethical maze that RPA pilots often find themselves in. The overarching debate about the morality of drone warfare, the issues of collateral damage, and the broader implications of a conflict where one side risks little to no personnel can lead to moral injuries. Such injuries occur when one perpetrates, witnesses, or fails to prevent actions that clash with their moral or ethical beliefs. Over time, these moral quandaries can lead to feelings of guilt, shame, and resentment.

As warfare continues to evolve, understanding the nuanced psychological implications of these changes is imperative. While RPAs offer undeniable strategic advantages, it's essential to recognize and address the unique challenges they pose to the human psyche. By doing so, military organizations can better support their personnel, ensuring their well-being while optimizing operational outcomes. The age of remote warfare, while distancing combatants from physical danger, brings them face-to-face with a new frontier of psychological challenges that need both acknowledgment and addressal.

Chapter 8: The Evolution of RPAs

Technological Advancements

The narrative surrounding Remotely Piloted Aircrafts (RPAs), often known colloquially as drones, cannot be fully understood without delving into their technological evolution. This journey from rudimentary unmanned flying machines to sophisticated, state-of-the-art combat and surveillance tools is a testament to both human ingenuity and the demands of modern warfare. By tracing the technological advancements of RPAs, we can better appreciate their current capabilities and anticipate the direction in which they are headed.

In the beginning, the concept of an unmanned aircraft was as rudimentary as one could imagine. Think of basic motorized kites or simple gliders equipped with cameras during the early 20th century. These were not the streamlined, efficient machines we have today but clunky, often unreliable contraptions. Their initial purpose was largely reconnaissance, capitalizing on their ability to traverse enemy lines without the risk of losing a human life.

However, as the 20th century progressed, so did the technological underpinnings of these devices. The introduction of radio technology in the mid-20th century was a game-changer. This meant that RPAs could be remotely controlled from a distance, effectively expanding their operational range and utility. The incorporation of radio technology not only expanded the horizons for these flying machines but also set the stage for their eventual transformation into formidable tools of warfare.

By the time the late 20th and early 21st centuries rolled around, the advancements in RPA technology were accelerating at an unprecedented pace. With the fusion of computer systems and enhanced aeronautical designs, RPAs became more agile, durable, and efficient. These were no longer just floating cameras; they had become multifaceted tools equipped with a suite of sensors, advanced communication systems, and even weaponry. The ability to carry out precision strikes from thousands of miles away became a reality, revolutionizing the very concept of engagement in conflict zones.

The enhancement in battery and propulsion technologies has also played a significant role in shaping the current state of RPAs. The introduction of energy-dense batteries and more efficient propulsion systems has extended the endurance and range of these aircraft. Some of the advanced models can now remain airborne for days, providing continuous surveillance or waiting for the opportune moment to strike.

Parallelly, the software that underpins RPA operations has seen transformative developments. Advanced algorithms now allow for better target recognition, threat analysis, and decision-making support. With the advent of artificial intelligence and machine learning, there's a burgeoning potential for RPAs to carry out complex missions with minimal human intervention, heralding the era of semi-autonomous or even fully autonomous operations.

Yet, it's not just the hardware and software that have seen monumental growth. The integration of satellite communication has bridged the gap between the RPA and its human operators, irrespective of their geographic locations. This has led to the concept of a global operations room where pilots situated in one part of the world can operate an RPA in a completely different region, all in real-time.

However, with every technological advancement comes a set of challenges and concerns. The proliferation of advanced RPAs has raised questions about aerial sovereignty, ethics in warfare, and the potential misuse of these tools. Moreover, as these systems become more autonomous, the dilemmas surrounding machine decision-making in life-and-death scenarios become more pronounced.

In retrospection, the technological trajectory of RPAs is a mirror to our broader societal, political, and ethical evolution. As they transition from simple observational tools to complex, integrated combat systems, RPAs encapsulate the confluence of technology and strategy. Their story is not just one of engineering marvels but also of the shifting paradigms of warfare and international relations in the 21st century.

Looking ahead, the fusion of nanotechnology, quantum computing, and advanced AI promises to further reshape the landscape of RPAs. As we stand on the cusp of these advancements, it behooves us to not only marvel at these technological wonders but also reflect upon the responsibilities they bestow upon us. In the evolution of RPAs, we find a mirror to our aspirations, our capabilities, and the profound dilemmas of our times.

The software infrastructure underpinning the functionality of Remotely Piloted Aircrafts (RPAs) has undeniably been at the forefront of their transformative evolution. This software, deeply intertwined with the hardware, can be likened to the brain behind the machine, dictating its behaviors, responses, and capabilities. As we delve deeper into the nuanced world of RPA software advancements, we'll uncover the layers of perception, control algorithms, and the shift towards autonomy that are redefining the scope and effectiveness of these airborne marvels.

Evolution of Perception Algorithms

In the initial stages, RPAs primarily relied on simple video feeds for reconnaissance. However, with the proliferation of advanced sensors, including infrared, radar, and even lidar, the sheer volume and complexity of data these aircrafts began to collect increased exponentially. To process this avalanche of information in real-time, sophisticated perception algorithms were developed.

These algorithms, often harnessing the power of machine learning, are trained to discern minute details from the sensor data. For instance, they can differentiate between a civilian vehicle and a military convoy based solely on infrared signatures or detect concealed anti-aircraft installations using subtle radar reflections. The objective is clear: enhance the RPA's ability to "see" and "understand" its environment in a more nuanced manner, ensuring that vital information doesn't go unnoticed.

Advanced Control and Decision-Making Algorithms

The journey from mere perception to actionable insight is bridged by advanced control algorithms. These algorithms take the raw data, process it, and then translate it into potential courses of action. For instance, when an RPA identifies a potential threat, control algorithms weigh the immediacy of the threat, the potential collateral damage, and even the RPA's current resource status (like fuel or ammunition) before suggesting a response.

But the marvel doesn't stop at suggestion; it extends to actual execution. Once a course of action is decided upon, either autonomously by the RPA or through human intervention, the software ensures the precise execution of the task. Whether it's a rapid evasive maneuver, the release of a countermeasure, or the precision-guided deployment of a weapon, the control algorithms ensure that the RPA's actions are both accurate and effective.

Advent of Semi and Fully Autonomous Drones

The natural progression in the RPA software evolution has been the shift towards autonomy. In semi-autonomous systems, while the RPA can perform a majority of its functions independently, critical decisions, especially those involving the use of lethal force, are reserved for human operators. This model provides a balance, ensuring rapid response times while keeping a human in the loop for ethical and strategic considerations.

Fully autonomous drones, a more controversial frontier, are designed to carry out entire missions without human intervention. These systems, while still in their nascent stages, rely heavily on artificial intelligence. They are trained using vast datasets, simulating countless scenarios to ensure that when faced with a real-world situation, they can make decisions that align with predefined strategic and ethical guidelines.

The move towards autonomy is not merely a technological aspiration; it's a strategic one. In environments where electronic warfare tools might compromise communication links, a fully autonomous drone can continue its mission without being rendered ineffective. Furthermore, in fast-evolving combat scenarios, the time taken for a human operator to analyze and respond might result in missed opportunities or increased risks. Autonomous systems can mitigate such delays.

However, the path to autonomy is riddled with challenges. There are ethical dilemmas to grapple with: can a machine be entrusted with life and death decisions? There are also technological hurdles. Ensuring that an autonomous system can reliably interpret complex, often ambiguous situations without error is no small feat.

The software ecosystem of RPAs is a realm of continuous innovation and exploration. As we push the boundaries of what these machines can perceive, decide, and execute, we also tread on profound philosophical terrains. The fusion of technology and ethics, strategy and software, presents a compelling, often challenging narrative, one that will shape the very future of airborne warfare and surveillance.

Integration of AI in RPAs

The fusion of nanotechnology, quantum computing, and advanced AI represents an epoch-making transformation in the realm of Remotely Piloted Aircrafts (RPAs). This amalgamation is not just about technology; it's a tapestry that intertwines the very fabric of engineering, physics, and cognitive science. Let's navigate through this intricate maze, understanding how these groundbreaking technologies are poised to redefine the future of RPAs and airborne warfare.

Nanotechnology: Miniaturization and Enhancement

Nanotechnology is fundamentally about manipulating matter at the atomic or molecular scale. For RPAs, this holds the promise of radical miniaturization while simultaneously enhancing functionality. Imagine drones the size of a dragonfly, equipped with sensors, cameras, and even miniature propulsion systems, all made feasible by nanotechnology. Such drones could be deployed for stealth surveillance, moving undetected in hostile environments.

But nanotechnology isn't just about creating 'nano-drones'. It's also about enhancing the capabilities of larger RPAs. By utilizing nanomaterials, we can envision aircrafts with lighter yet stronger frames, leading to increased maneuverability and endurance. Nano-enhanced coatings could reduce radar signatures, rendering the RPAs stealthier against detection systems.

Quantum Computing: Ultra-Fast Processing and Cryptography

Quantum computing is a paradigm shift from traditional computing. At its core, it harnesses the principles of quantum mechanics to process vast amounts of data simultaneously. For RPAs, this translates to dramatically improved data processing and decision-making speeds. In a battlefield scenario, where split-second decisions can determine outcomes, quantum-powered RPAs would have a distinct advantage, analyzing complex data streams in real-time, ranging from meteorological data to enemy positioning.

Moreover, quantum computing holds a special place in the realm of cryptography. As electronic warfare and cyber-espionage become increasingly sophisticated, the encryption methods safeguarding communication between RPAs and their control stations become crucial. Quantum cryptography, touted as 'unhackable' due to the fundamental properties of quantum mechanics, can ensure that RPA communications remain secure, even against adversaries equipped with advanced decryption tools.

Advanced AI: Autonomy, Learning, and Adaptability

The term 'AI' often gets thrown around as a buzzword, but its application in RPAs is tangible and transformative. Leveraging deep learning and neural networks, advanced AI allows RPAs to 'learn' from each mission, improving their strategies and tactics continuously. Whether it's optimizing flight paths based on past reconnaissance data or adapting in real-time to unforeseen obstacles, AI-driven RPAs become smarter with each flight.

Furthermore, the integration of AI facilitates a more nuanced level of autonomy. These RPAs could potentially make complex decisions based on vast datasets, weighing mission objectives against potential risks. While there will always be a debate about the ethical considerations of such autonomy, especially in combat scenarios, the technological capability is fast becoming a reality.

The Convergence: A Symphony of Technologies

When these three technologies — nanotechnology, quantum computing, and advanced AI — converge, the result is nothing short of revolutionary. Picture an RPA, its frame enhanced by nanomaterials, making it lightweight and stealthy. Inside, a quantum computer processes vast streams of data at unparalleled speeds, encrypted securely against any breaches. Guiding this RPA's every move is an AI, trained on countless missions, constantly learning, adapting, and making decisions based on a vast reservoir of knowledge.

In this new era, RPAs would not just be tools; they'd be highly sophisticated entities, capable of feats that would have seemed like science fiction just a few decades ago. The strategic implications for defense, reconnaissance, and warfare are profound. But with great power comes great responsibility. As we stand on the brink of this new dawn, the onus is on policymakers, technologists, and military strategists to ensure that this power is harnessed responsibly, ethically, and in the best interests of peace and security.

Chapter 9: Beyond the Military: The Civilian Uses of RPAs

While the military applications of Remotely Piloted Aircrafts (RPAs) have undeniably been at the forefront of media and academic discussions, it's imperative to recognize the vast, transformative, and often less controversial impact of these devices in civilian sectors. The footprint of RPAs in non-military domains is burgeoning, influencing sectors as diverse as agriculture, entertainment, health, and transportation. By tapping into the multifaceted capabilities of these machines, society at large stands on the precipice of a technological renaissance, unlocking efficiencies and capabilities hitherto deemed unattainable.

Let us embark on an expansive journey, delving into the myriad ways RPAs are revolutionizing the civilian landscape, from the furrows of farmlands to the congested arteries of urban centers.

Agriculture

The agrarian sector, often viewed as a bastion of tradition, is undergoing a quiet revolution, thanks in no small part to RPAs. Farmers are harnessing these airborne marvels to monitor vast tracts of land, assessing crop health, soil moisture levels, and even spotting potential pest infestations. With high-resolution cameras and advanced sensors, RPAs can detect subtle changes in vegetation, allowing for timely interventions. This isn't merely about optimizing yields; it's a holistic approach to sustainable farming. By pinpointing exactly where resources like water or fertilizers are needed, wastage is minimized, ensuring that the delicate balance of our ecosystems is maintained.

Healthcare

In regions where terrestrial infrastructure is wanting or in cases of natural calamities, RPAs emerge as veritable lifelines. There have been instances where RPAs have expedited the delivery of critical medicines, blood units, and even organs for transplantation, circumventing treacherous terrains or congested urban mazes. This isn't merely about speed; it's about making healthcare accessible, about ensuring that a patient in a remote village isn't denied life-saving intervention simply due to geographical constraints.

Entertainment

The cinematic world has always been about capturing imaginations, transporting audiences to realms beyond their mundane realities. RPAs have given filmmakers a potent tool to achieve just this. Aerial shots, once the prerogative of big-budget productions that could afford helicopters, are now within reach of indie filmmakers, thanks to cost-effective RPAs. These devices can weave through narrow alleyways, soar above majestic landscapes, or hover tantalizingly close to a dramatic moment, offering perspectives that are as novel as they are captivating.

Transportation and Logistics

E-commerce giants and logistics companies are increasingly eyeing RPAs as a solution to the last-mile delivery conundrum. The vision is tantalizing: customers receiving their packages from the sky, with RPAs gently depositing parcels at predetermined locations. Beyond the obvious allure of speed and efficiency, this paradigm holds environmental promise. As RPAs become more energy-efficient and increasingly rely on renewable energy sources, the carbon footprint of deliveries could be drastically reduced, offering a greener alternative to road-bound delivery vehicles.

Urban Planning and Infrastructure Monitoring

City planners and civil engineers are increasingly leveraging RPAs for tasks ranging from traffic pattern analyses to structural health monitoring of towering skyscrapers and expansive bridges. The agility of these devices, coupled with their ability to carry a range of sensors, allows for detailed, real-time insights. For burgeoning metropolises grappling with the challenges of urbanization, RPAs offer data-driven solutions, ensuring that growth is both sustainable and strategic.

Conservation and Environmental Monitoring

RPAs are playing a pivotal role in conservation efforts worldwide. Whether it's tracking endangered species in vast national parks or monitoring deforestation in critical biomes, these devices offer an unobtrusive method to gather essential data. For conservationists, the ability to remotely monitor sensitive habitats without physically intruding is invaluable, ensuring that their efforts to protect are not inadvertently causing disruption.

Rescue and Relief Efforts

Natural calamities and unforeseen disasters can strike with little to no warning. In the wake of such events, the immediacy of the response can often be the difference between life and death. RPAs have emerged as indispensable assets in such scenarios. Whether it's the aftermath of an earthquake, where structures have crumbled, trapping potential survivors, or flood scenarios where vast areas are rendered inaccessible, RPAs offer a rapid, efficient, and safe means to assess the situation. With thermal imaging capabilities, for instance, RPAs can identify heat signatures in rubble, pointing rescue teams precisely where survivors might be trapped. In flood scenarios, they offer a bird's-eye view of the affected regions, enabling efficient coordination of relief efforts and ensuring resources such as food, water, and medicine are directed where they are needed most.

Real Estate and Land Surveys

The real estate sector is witnessing an aerial revolution, all thanks to RPAs. Prospective buyers can now get aerial views of properties, offering a comprehensive perspective that ground tours might miss. Beyond just showcasing properties, RPAs are invaluable for land surveys, especially in terrains that are challenging to access. For realtors, developers, and landowners, the implications are profound. Land disputes, often stemming from ambiguous boundaries, can be efficiently resolved with the detailed imagery RPAs provide. Moreover, developers can assess the viability of construction projects, gauging factors like drainage, access routes, and potential obstructions long before the first brick is laid.

Scientific Research

Scientists across disciplines are harnessing the power of RPAs. In archaeology, for instance, these devices are uncovering relics of bygone eras, offering aerial perspectives of excavation sites, and even using sophisticated ground-penetrating radars to identify potential sites of interest beneath the surface. Meteorologists are deploying RPAs into storm systems, gathering real-time data that not only furthers our understanding of climatic phenomena but also improves the accuracy of weather forecasts. Oceanographers, too, are not far behind, using specialized RPAs to study marine ecosystems, track migratory patterns of marine species, and even assess the health of coral reefs.

Journalism and Reporting

The world of journalism has always been about capturing the essence of the moment, about presenting stories in their most visceral form. RPAs are offering journalists a tool to achieve this with even greater efficacy. Whether it's covering massive public gatherings, tracking the progress of a wildfire, or offering real-time insights into conflict zones, RPAs are enabling journalists to present a more comprehensive narrative. The safety implications are undeniable. In volatile regions, where the physical presence of journalists can be fraught with danger, RPAs offer a means to cover stories without direct exposure to potential harm.

Energy and Utilities

The energy sector, encompassing the vast infrastructures of oil, gas, and electricity, finds RPAs to be invaluable. Monitoring pipelines stretching over hundreds of miles, inspecting towering electricity pylons, or assessing the structural integrity of offshore oil rigs, RPAs offer a safer, efficient, and more cost-effective alternative to traditional methods. The implications for safety and maintenance are profound. Early detection of issues, be it a leak in a pipeline or a fault in an electricity line, can prevent potential disasters.

As we traverse the myriad civilian applications of RPAs, it becomes abundantly clear that we are only scratching the surface of their potential. Every sector, every niche, every facet of our daily lives stands poised on the cusp of an aerial revolution. Yet, with this expansive potential comes the responsibility of judicious use. As societies globally grapple with the challenges and opportunities RPAs present, it is incumbent upon us to navigate this new frontier with foresight, ensuring that the promise of these devices is realized, while the challenges they present are methodically addressed. The future of RPAs in civilian sectors shines bright, heralding an era where the sky is not just a frontier but a canvas of endless possibilities.

The civilian applications of RPAs are as vast as they are transformative. Every sector, every discipline, every facet of human endeavor stands to gain from these devices. But as with all potent tools, responsible use is the watchword. As we embrace the myriad possibilities RPAs offer, it's imperative to navigate the ethical, privacy, and safety concerns that inevitably accompany them. In this dance of technology and humanity, it's upon us to ensure that the rhythm is harmonious, that the promises are realized, and that the challenges are judiciously addressed.

Chapter 10: A Glimpse into the Future

Next Generation of RPAs

The trajectory of Remotely Piloted Aircrafts (RPAs) has been nothing short of meteoric. From their nascent stages as rudimentary surveillance tools to their current stature as indispensable assets for a myriad of tasks, RPAs have revolutionized numerous sectors. But, as with all technological marvels, the RPA's story is far from over. We stand on the precipice of another wave of advancements that promise to reshape the very fabric of aerial operations. This chapter embarks on a speculative journey, charting the potential future of RPAs and envisioning a world where the sky is replete with possibilities.

The innate human curiosity, which has for centuries driven us to push boundaries and transcend limits, is ever-present in the realm of RPAs. As technology continues to evolve, we find ourselves intertwining various advancements, merging disciplines, and creating devices that once resided solely in the realm of science fiction. The next generation of RPAs promises not just to be an iteration of their predecessors, but a reimagining of what aerial devices can achieve.

One of the most tantalizing prospects on the horizon is the application of swarm intelligence to RPAs. Drawing inspiration from nature, where birds flock in unison and fish move in synchronized schools, swarm intelligence envisions multiple RPAs operating in tandem, communicating in real-time, and executing complex tasks collectively. Such a paradigm shift moves away from the individual capabilities of a single RPA and instead harnesses the collective might of many. This not only amplifies the efficacy of operations but also offers redundancies, where the failure of a single unit doesn't jeopardize the entire mission.

The Achilles' heel of most RPAs has been their reliance on traditional energy sources, limiting their operational time and tethering them to recharging or refueling stations. The future, however, paints a picture of energy autonomy. With strides being made in solar technology, envision RPAs equipped with advanced photovoltaic cells, capable of drawing energy from the sun during daylight and relying on efficient battery systems at night. Such advancements not only prolong operational time but also align RPAs with the global shift towards sustainable technologies.

While current RPAs are no strangers to artificial intelligence, the future holds promise for even more advanced AI integrations. Think of RPAs capable of complex decision-making processes, analyzing vast swathes of data in real-time, and executing tasks with minimal human intervention. Such advancements transform RPAs from mere tools to entities, ones capable of dynamic responses based on the environment they operate in. The implications for surveillance, reconnaissance, and even civilian operations like traffic management and urban planning are profound.

The RPAs of tomorrow won't just be reliant on advanced cameras for their operations. The integration of a plethora of sensors, from thermal and infrared to ultrasonic and LIDAR, will grant RPAs a sensory perception that rivals, if not surpasses, human capabilities. This enhances their operational efficacy in a myriad of environments, from the pitch-black caverns of underground operations to the blinding glare of desert reconnaissance.

The siloed operation of RPAs is set to be a thing of the past. Envision a world where RPAs seamlessly integrate with other technologies, be it ground-based autonomous vehicles or deep-sea exploration drones. Such interactivity ensures a cohesive operational framework, where data from one platform can inform the actions of another, creating a mesh of interconnected devices working towards a unified goal.

The tapestry of the future, woven with the threads of innovation, ingenuity, and inspiration, promises a realm where RPAs are not just devices but an intrinsic part of our societal fabric. As we peer into this future, it becomes evident that the journey of RPAs is not just about technological advancements but also about reimagining our relationship with the skies. A realm once reserved for birds and the occasional aircraft is now a canvas of endless possibilities, waiting to be painted with the brushstrokes of the next generation of RPAs.

My Vision for the Future of Remote Aviation

The dawn of aviation in the early 20th century heralded an era of unbridled possibilities. Mankind took to the skies, leaving behind the confines of terrestrial limitations. Yet, as profound as that era was, the advent of remote aviation brought forth a paradigm shift of equal magnitude, if not more. The notion of controlling an aircraft, not from within its cockpit, but from miles away, was a leap of faith into the chasm of technological advancements. As we stand on the precipice of further innovations, my vision for the future of remote aviation is both a dreamer's fantasy and an engineer's calculated prediction, one that is expansive in its scope and groundbreaking in its implications.

In the foreseeable future, I imagine a world where the line between pilot and remotely piloted aircraft (RPA) is not just blurred but is virtually nonexistent. This isn't to suggest the eradication of human input; rather, it underscores a seamless integration of human intuition with machine precision. Advanced neural interfaces could pave the way for pilots to connect with their machines at a cognitive level, interpreting neural signals into flight commands. The result? An RPA responding not just to joystick movements but to the very thoughts and instincts of its pilot.

Surveillance, the cornerstone of many remote aviation operations, will undergo a transformative evolution. Instead of individual RPAs embarking on surveillance missions, the future may witness the deployment of aerial networks, comprising thousands of micro-drones. These drones, operating in perfect synchrony, would provide real-time, 360-degree coverage of vast areas. Imagine the intricacies of a bustling city or the expansive swathes of a forest being monitored in minute detail, ensuring both urban security and environmental conservation.

While the present-day remote aviation landscape is dominated by human-controlled operations, the future could usher in an era of semi-autonomous and even fully autonomous missions. Advanced artificial intelligence systems, armed with deep learning capabilities, will allow RPAs to understand their environment, make split-second decisions, and even adapt to unforeseen challenges. While the notion of machines operating without human intervention may seem daunting to some, the rigorous protocols and safety nets in place would ensure that autonomy does not come at the expense of safety.

One of the most significant challenges that remote aviation currently grapples with is the coexistence of manned and unmanned aircraft in shared airspace. My vision for the future sees a harmonious integration, where both entities coalesce into a unified aerial ecosystem. Advanced air traffic management systems, bolstered by quantum computing capabilities, would ensure that the skies are orchestrated with the precision of a maestro leading an orchestra, with each entity, be it manned or unmanned, playing its part to perfection.

The domain of remote aviation need not be confined solely to our planet. As we set our sights on the vast expanse of space, remote aviation could very well be the linchpin in exploring celestial bodies. Lunar or Martian drones, controlled from Earth or from orbiting satellites, could provide invaluable insights into these terrains, proving to be the vanguard of human colonization endeavors.

One of the most profound impacts of the future of remote aviation could be its democratization. No longer would piloting be the exclusive domain of a select few. With the right training and the advancement of intuitive control interfaces, anyone, irrespective of physical limitations, could take to the skies, albeit remotely. This narrative of inclusivity would make the skies a canvas for all of humanity to paint its aspirations upon.

The future of remote aviation is not just about technological innovations; it is a testament to human ingenuity and our insatiable quest for progress. As we soar into this future, we carry with us the lessons of the past, the aspirations of the present, and the limitless possibilities of tomorrow. It is a journey that promises both challenges and rewards, but above all, it promises the continuation of mankind's age-old affair with the skies. The horizon beckons, and with remote aviation as our steed, we are poised to traverse it in ways we have only dared to dream of.

Conclusion

Reflections on a Career in RPAs

In the vast tapestry of human endeavors, each stitch represents an individual journey, a singular narrative that, when woven together, creates the rich fabric of our shared history. My career in RPAs, spanning over several transformative decades, represents but one of these stitches, albeit one that has been intricately and passionately interlaced with the evolving narrative of aviation.

The trajectory of my involvement with RPAs began, like many pioneering ventures, with a mixture of skepticism and curiosity. In the early days, the notion of a remotely piloted aircraft was, for many, an esoteric concept, a fantastical vision drawn from the pages of science fiction. Yet, for those of us who were fortunate enough to be at the forefront of this technological renaissance, it was a glimpse into a future teeming with possibilities. The early RPAs, while rudimentary by today's standards, were revolutionary in their time. They signaled the dawning of a new era, where the boundaries of aviation were no longer constrained by the physical limitations of human pilots.

Throughout my career, I bore witness to, and played an integral part in, the rapid evolution of RPAs. From their initial roles in reconnaissance and surveillance to their eventual adoption in combat and beyond, RPAs transformed from mere tools to indispensable assets in a myriad of operations. The technical leaps were astounding. What began as basic remote-controlled aircraft soon integrated cutting-edge sensors, advanced AI-driven algorithms, and capabilities that blurred the lines between man and machine.

However, beyond the technological marvels, what truly stood out for me was the profound impact RPAs had on the human element of warfare and surveillance. The duality of being both detached from immediate danger, yet deeply immersed in the operational theater, presented a unique psychological conundrum. There were moments of unparalleled elation, such as when an RPA, under my control, successfully thwarted a potential threat, saving countless lives. Conversely, there were instances of introspection and moral dilemmas, particularly when the lines between right and wrong became blurred in the fog of war.

The landscape of remote aviation was not merely confined to military applications. As I navigated through the intricacies of my career, I was constantly reminded of the vast civilian potential of RPAs. From agricultural monitoring to disaster relief, the adaptability and versatility of RPAs opened doors to domains that were previously deemed inaccessible. This seamless fusion of military precision with civilian benevolence was a testament to the boundless potential of human ingenuity.

Yet, for all the accolades and advancements, the journey was not devoid of challenges. The rapid pace of technological evolution invariably brought forth questions of ethics, governance, and accountability. The very nature of RPAs, operating in a realm that was both tangible and virtual, presented challenges that were as much philosophical as they were technical. Each mission, each flight, was a lesson in navigating these intricate nuances, striving for a balance between duty and morality.

As I reflect upon my career, I am filled with a profound sense of gratitude. Gratitude for having been a part of a revolutionary chapter in aviation history, gratitude for the countless individuals who shared this journey with me, and above all, gratitude for the lessons, both joyous and challenging, that enriched my professional and personal life. The world of RPAs, much like the vast expanse of the skies it operates in, is boundless in its potential. As I hang up my virtual flight gloves, I do so with the hope that the future custodians of this domain will soar to even greater heights, guided by the twin beacons of innovation and integrity.

In the final reckoning, a career in RPAs is not just about flying machines; it's about charting the uncharted, embracing the unknown, and above all, believing in the limitless potential of human-machine synergy. As I bid adieu to this chapter of my life, I do so with a heart full of memories, a mind brimming with experiences, and a soul that will forever remain tethered to the ethereal world of remote aviation. The skies beckon, and while my active journey may have concluded, the echoes of my flights will resonate for eternity.

The Changing Face of Aviation and Warfare

In the annals of human history, few domains have witnessed as dramatic a transformation in such a condensed time frame as that of aviation and warfare. When one steps back to cast a contemplative eye over the cascading events, technological leaps, and paradigm shifts that have punctuated the trajectory of these fields, one cannot help but be struck by a profound sense of awe. From the nascent flutterings of mankind's earliest flying machines to the hyper-advanced remotely piloted aircraft of today, the evolution of aviation has been nothing short of meteoric. This trajectory, intertwined inextricably with the shifting sands of warfare, presents a tale that is both triumphant and cautionary.

Aviation, in its purest form, began as an endeavor to fulfill one of humanity's oldest dreams: the dream to soar like birds, to break the shackles of terrestrial existence and embrace the boundless skies. The early pioneers of aviation, driven by a combination of audacity and ingenuity, laid the foundational stones upon which the magnificent edifice of modern aviation would be built. With each passing decade, aircraft became faster, more reliable, and capable of feats previously deemed impossible. However, it was not long before the potential of aviation as a tool of warfare was recognized, and thus began the inexorable march towards harnessing the skies for martial purposes.

The two World Wars that marred the 20th century underscored the criticality of air superiority in the theater of conflict. Battlefields were no longer confined to land and sea; the skies became arenas of intense dogfights, strategic bombings, and reconnaissance missions. The jet engine, radar systems, and advances in aerodynamics revolutionized the capacities of combat aircraft. Yet, for all the advancements, these machines were still intrinsically tied to the human pilots who commanded them, individuals whose bravery and skill became the stuff of legends.

However, as the world transitioned into the latter half of the 20th century and edged into the 21st, the landscape of aviation and warfare underwent another seismic shift. The introduction of remotely piloted aircraft systems, or RPAs, represented a confluence of technological advancements and strategic imperatives. No longer were aircraft bound by the physiological limitations of their human pilots. RPAs, with their capacity to loiter for extended periods, their precision targeting capabilities, and their ability to operate in environments deemed too risky for manned aircraft, heralded a new era in aerial warfare.

Yet, this technological leap did not come without its set of complexities. The very detachment that RPAs afforded, the ability to project power without immediate personal risk, brought forth a plethora of ethical, psychological, and strategic conundrums. The narrative of warfare transitioned from the visceral, immediate experiences of pilots in cockpits to the sterile, almost video-game-like operations of drone pilots stationed thousands of miles away from their targets. This detachment, while tactically advantageous, engendered debates about the morality of remote warfare, about the psychological toll it exacts on the operators, and about the broader implications for global geopolitics.

Furthermore, the rapid advancements in artificial intelligence, quantum computing, and sensor technology have poised the domain of aviation and warfare on the cusp of another transformative phase. The nascent developments in fully autonomous drones, capable of making decisions without human intervention, present both tantalizing possibilities and daunting challenges. As these machines grow smarter and more independent, the lines between human judgment and algorithmic determinations begin to blur, raising profound questions about accountability, control, and the very essence of warfare.

In reflecting upon the trajectory of aviation and warfare, one is reminded of the dual nature of technological progress. On one hand, it offers the promise of a better, more efficient future, a world where conflicts can be resolved with minimal human cost, where the vastness of the skies can be harnessed for the betterment of all. On the other hand, it presents challenges that test the very fabric of our moral, ethical, and strategic foundations.

As this chapter in the grand tapestry of human history continues to unfold, it behooves us to approach the future with a blend of optimism and caution. For in the delicate balance between progress and prudence lies the path to a future where the skies, once a realm of dreams and aspirations, continue to inspire, challenge, and elevate humanity to new heights. The changing face of aviation and warfare is not just a testament to human ingenuity but also a reminder of our responsibilities as custodians of this ever-evolving legacy.

A: Glossary of Key Terms

- Aerodynamics: The study of the properties of moving air and the interaction between the air and solid bodies moving through it.

- AI (Artificial Intelligence): The capability of a machine or software to imitate intelligent human behavior, such as decision-making, speech recognition, and problem-solving.

- Algorithm: A set procedure or formula for solving a problem, especially by a computer.

- Autonomous Drone: An unmanned aircraft that can fly and perform tasks without human intervention, relying on onboard algorithms and sensors.

- Bandwidth: The capacity of a radio frequency channel for data transmission. In RPAs, this term often refers to the capacity for transmitting data between the aircraft and the ground control station.

- Cockpit: The front compartment of an aircraft from where the pilot controls the machine. In RPAs, this might refer to the virtual interface or the ground control station.

- Combat Air Patrol (CAP): An aircraft patrol provided over an objective area, the force protected, the critical area of a combat zone, or an air defense area.

- Data Link: The means of connecting one location to another for the purpose of transmitting and receiving data, especially crucial in the communication between RPAs and their control stations.

- Electro-optical Sensors: Devices that detect and measure light waves, converting them into electronic signals for analysis or transmission.

- Flight Envelope: The combination of limits within which an aircraft can safely fly, considering altitude, airspeed, and other factors.

- Ground Control Station (GCS): The equipment designed to control drones remotely from the ground.

- ISR (Intelligence, Surveillance, and Reconnaissance): The synchronized and integrated capability to observe, detect, and identify pertinent information and subsequently provide this data to leaders for decision-making.

- Loitering: The ability of an aircraft, particularly drones, to remain in flight over a particular area for extended periods.

- Nanotechnology: The manipulation of individual atoms and molecules to create new structures, materials, and devices on the nanometer scale.

- Quantum Computing: A type of computation that uses qubits (quantum bits) instead of the typical binary bits to perform operations, allowing for vastly more complex and faster calculations.

- RPAs (Remotely Piloted Aircraft Systems): A subset of unmanned aircraft systems that are operated by a pilot via a ground control system.

- Stealth Technology: Techniques used with aircraft, ships, and missiles to make them less visible (or invisible) to radar and other detection methods.

- Telemetry: The process of recording and transmitting readings of an instrument for the purpose of remotely monitoring various conditions or situations.

- UAV (Unmanned Aerial Vehicle): An aircraft that operates without a human pilot onboard, typically controlled remotely or autonomously.

- Waypoint: A specific geographical location through which a vehicle, especially an aircraft, is routed, serving as a guide for navigation.

The above glossary serves as a foundational understanding for many of the terms and concepts discussed throughout the context of aviation, RPAs, and the nexus of technology and warfare. Given the dynamic nature of this field, the definitions and terminologies are subject to evolution and expansion as new advancements and revelations emerge.

Appendix B: Relevant International Laws and Regulations on RPAs

1. International Civil Aviation Organization (ICAO): The ICAO began exploring the use of drone technology as early as 2005, culminating in a 2011 report. The ICAO states that a UAS should demonstrate equivalent levels of safety as manned aircraft and thus meet relevant government rules for flight and flight equipment. The ICAO further distinguishes between autonomous aircraft and remotely-piloted aircraft (RPA), and anticipates that only RPA "will be able to integrate into the international civil aviation system in the foreseeable future".

2. Unmanned Aircraft Systems (UAS) Advisory Group: Set up in 2015 by the United Nations' civil aviation arm to draw up global rules and regulations for the safe use of unmanned aircraft. The team comprises countries such as the United States, France, and China, as well as industry bodies like the global pilots' association.

3. European Union (EU): The EU implemented unmanned aircraft regulation starting on December 31, 2020. The first step for a drone operator/remote pilot would be to register in the country in which they live, or have their main place of business. EASA also issued guidelines for the management of drone incidents at airports, and rules for air traffic management kicked in as of July 1, 2021.

4. Australia: UAV operators are required to keep their drones at least 30m from people, structures, and buildings, and shouldn't be operated in a way that creates a hazard.

5. Brazil: The National Civil Aviation Agency regulated the operation of drones through the Brazilian Special Civil Aviation Regulation No. 94/2017 (RBAC-E No. 94/2017).

6. Canada: Introduced regulations in 2019 that require all drones over 250 grams to be registered and insured. Operators are required to be of a minimum age and pass an exam to get a license.

7. France: Overflights of nuclear power plants are illegal. The punishment is a year in prison and a fine of €75,000 if an aircraft comes within 5 km horizontally or 1 km vertically of a plant.

8. Hong Kong: No-fly zones have been declared in several areas, including Victoria Harbour, country parks, the airport, military sites, prisons, and government-run leisure facilities. The government is proposing to introduce regulations that will broadly follow American standards, which might require all drones above a certain weight to be registered.

9. India: Permission from WPC is required for importing any radio-controlled equipment, including drones/UAVs.

Acknowledgements

It is a rare privilege to journey into the complexities of the ever-evolving world of Remotely Piloted Aircrafts (RPAs) and to share this exploration in a format that is accessible to the masses. This endeavor, as sprawling and intricate as the subject itself, would not have been possible without the involvement, dedication, and passion of countless individuals.

First and foremost, I'd like to express my deepest gratitude to the men and women of the armed forces, particularly those who have served alongside me in various capacities related to RPAs. From those tense moments in control rooms to the extensive debriefing sessions, their unwavering dedication to the mission and their invaluable insights have informed much of the material in this book.

Special appreciation goes to Lieutenant Colonel James V. Hartinger, whose knowledge and expertise have been a guiding light throughout my career. Jim, your tales from the earliest days of drone warfare and your thoughtful reflections on where the industry might head provided the much-needed historical context to this volume.

I must also acknowledge my esteemed colleagues at Greyhat Intelligence & Investigative Solutions. The team's unwavering support, particularly during the challenging phases of this book's creation, has been nothing short of inspirational. Their behind-the-scenes efforts, from research to validating technical specifics, have been invaluable.

To Professor Richard Pildes, whose incisive quote sparked many a discussion and reflection, I thank you for your academic rigor and your willingness to challenge established narratives. Your work in the field has been a beacon for many of us.

A heartfelt nod to my editorial team led by Karen L. Mitchell. Karen, your uncanny ability to navigate the intricate labyrinths of military jargon and transform them into readable prose has been a godsend. To the rest of the team – your patience, dedication, and commitment to preserving the essence of my experiences while making them relatable are genuinely commendable.

To my family – my anchors and my constants. Your unwavering faith in my endeavors, even when they took me miles away from home, both physically and mentally, has been the wind beneath my wings. Your love, patience, and understanding, especially during the late nights and missed occasions, made this journey a tad bit easier.

Lastly, to the readers and enthusiasts of aviation technology and warfare – thank you for your curiosity and engagement. This book is, at its core, a tribute to the spirit of exploration, innovation, and the relentless pursuit of progress. I hope it provides you with a lens to look into a world that, though remote, impacts us in profound ways.

It is often said that it takes a village, and in the case of this book, it couldn't be truer. My heartfelt thanks to each individual who played a part, big or small, in bringing this vision to life. Onward and upward.

Author's Bio

Lt. Col. John "Hawkeye" Mitchell is a distinguished veteran of the Air Force and a preeminent figure in the complex world of global security and warfare. Enlisting fresh out of college, John quickly rose through the ranks due to his exceptional flying skills, strategic acumen, and a keen understanding of the interplay between technology and modern warfare. As a pilot, he commanded numerous missions using Remotely Piloted Aircrafts (RPAs), contributing significantly to the evolution of aerial warfare.

Upon his honorable discharge from the Air Force, John's deep expertise was quickly sought after by the Central Intelligence Agency (CIA). Working as a contractor, he was instrumental in executing covert operations across volatile terrains, utilizing a combination of on-ground intelligence and state-of-the-art aerial surveillance technologies. His assignments with the CIA, often cloaked in secrecy, took him to critical hotspots around the globe where he played pivotal roles in shaping key outcomes.

Subsequent to his tenure with the CIA, John transitioned into the challenging world of Private Military Contracting (PMC). His operations spanned the volatile theatres of the war on terror – from the labyrinthine alleys of the Middle East and the treacherous terrains of Africa to the dense jungles of Asia. In this capacity, he not only led combat missions but also trained militia, ensuring local forces were adequately equipped to maintain stability once primary operations concluded.

In "The Reaper's Flight: My Life Behind the MQ-9 Reaper", John melds his firsthand experiences with a broader examination of the role of RPAs in modern warfare, blending gritty personal anecdotes with meticulous technical details.

Off the battlefield and away from the high-stakes world of security contracting, John is a passionate advocate for veterans, focusing on their mental health and reintegration into civilian life. He also engages in public speaking, sharing insights from his diverse career and shedding light on the shadowy world of global conflict.

A father of two and a dedicated husband, John currently resides in Virginia, where he enjoys the serenity of nature, a stark contrast to the tumultuous terrains he once navigated. This book is not just a chronicle of his professional journey but also a tribute to the countless unsung heroes who risk their lives in the name of peace and security.

Don't miss out!

Visit the website below and you can sign up to receive emails whenever John 'Hawkeye' Mitchell publishes a new book. There's no charge and no obligation.

https://books2read.com/r/B-A-CROAB-UWHOC

Did you love *The Reaper's Flight: My Life Behind The MQ-9 Reaper*? Then you should read *The Insider's Guide to Securities Law: Navigating the Intricacies of Public and Private Offerings*[1] by Josh Luberisse!

[2]

Navigate the intricate world of private equity and venture capital with "The Insider's Guide to Securities Law: Navigating the Intricacies of Public and Private Offerings." This comprehensive guidebook illuminates the complexities of the industry, serving as an essential resource for legal practitioners, investment professionals, and entrepreneurs alike.

Venture into the fascinating domain of fund formation, understand the roles of limited and general partners, and uncover the strategic aspects of tax structuring. Get acquainted with the key regulatory authorities overseeing the industry, including the Securities and

1. https://books2read.com/u/31VK1M

2. https://books2read.com/u/31VK1M

Exchange Commission (SEC), the Financial Industry Regulatory Authority (FINRA), and the Commodity Futures Trading Commission (CFTC).

Delve deeper into the regulatory landscape, exploring crucial compliance requirements, the essentialities of fiduciary duty, and the impact of the JOBS Act and other significant laws. Grasp the essentials of Anti-Money Laundering (AML) and Know Your Customer (KYC) compliance, and learn how to navigate through the processes of sourcing and closing deals, conducting due diligence, and managing and exiting investments effectively.

"The Insider's Guide to Securities Law" offers practical insights, actionable strategies, and a detailed glossary of key terms, making the labyrinth of private equity and venture capital law accessible to both seasoned professionals and newcomers. Embark on a journey through the dynamic landscape of global finance with confidence and insight with this indispensable guide.

About the Author

Lt. Col. John "Hawkeye" Mitchell is a distinguished veteran of the Air Force and a preeminent figure in the complex world of global security and warfare. Enlisting fresh out of college, John quickly rose through the ranks due to his exceptional flying skills, strategic acumen, and a keen understanding of the interplay between technology and modern warfare. As a pilot, he commanded numerous missions using Remotely Piloted Aircrafts, contributing significantly to the evolution of aerial warfare.

Upon his honorable discharge from the Air Force, John's deep expertise was quickly sought after by the Central Intelligence Agency (CIA). Working as a contractor, he was instrumental in executing covert operations across volatile terrains, utilizing a combination of on-ground intelligence and state-of-the-art aerial surveillance technologies. His assignments with the CIA, often cloaked in secrecy, took him to critical hotspots around the globe where he played pivotal roles in shaping key outcomes.

Subsequent to his tenure with the CIA, John transitioned into the challenging world of Private Military Contracting (PMC). His operations spanned the volatile theatres of the war on terror – from the labyrinthine alleys of the Middle East and the treacherous terrains of Africa to the dense jungles of Asia. In this capacity, he not only led combat missions but also trained militia, ensuring local forces were adequately equipped to maintain stability once primary operations concluded.

Off the battlefield and away from the high-stakes world of security contracting, John is a passionate advocate for veterans, focusing on their mental health and reintegration into civilian life. He also engages in public speaking, sharing insights from his diverse career and shedding light on the shadowy world of global conflict.

A father of two and a dedicated husband, John currently resides in Virginia, where he enjoys the serenity of nature, a stark contrast to the tumultuous terrains he once navigated. This book is not just a chronicle of his professional journey but also a tribute to the countless unsung heroes who risk their lives in the name of peace and security.

About the Publisher

Fortis Novum Mundum, LLC is an independent black-owned publishing company focused on publishing work of non-fiction by independent authors.

Our publishing professionals are committed to assisting authors in creating their best work and exploring fresh avenues for disseminating literature and ideas to readers around the world. Our goal is to give writers the widest possible audience by expanding our reach internationally, adopting cutting-edge technological advances, and working closely with them throughout the entire publishing process, from editing and layout to publicity and sales to printing and shipping. We also defend the rights of our writers and promote free speech to make sure their words are heard far beyond the bounds of a book and into the fabric of communities and societies around the world.

Milton Keynes UK
Ingram Content Group UK Ltd.
UKHW010642021023
429777UK00001B/54

9 798223 702559